THE UNSTOPPABLE EDDIE FUGATE

GEOFFREY STEELE

ISBN (eBook): 979-8-9880648-0-0
ISBN (Paperback): 979-8-9880648-1-7
ISBN (Hardcover): 979-8-9880648-2-4
ISBN (Large Print Paperback): 979-8-9880648-3-1
Library of Congress Control Number: 2023910087

Title Production by The Book Whisperer

Cover Design by Jane Dixon-Smith

To Kay,
Jim and Lori

AN IMPORTANT NOTE TO THE READER

Early chapters take place at the Orient State Institute, a long-since-closed institution for individuals with intellectual disabilities in Pickaway County, Ohio. It existed at a time in our history when accepted notions about what constituted a disability, how to care for the disabled, what they might be capable of accomplishing, and even what to call them were very different from what they are today. The protagonist in this story was a resident of this institution as a young boy. But because in the years since his release, he has unfailingly refused to discuss his time there, the narrative in this first section was pieced together largely from conversations with former staff. As the story progresses, it more closely conforms to actual events, many of which were witnessed by the author. The names of many of the characters have been changed.

Geoffrey Steele

CHAPTER ONE

2012

Eddie Fugate sat at his kitchen table, concentrating fully on the task at hand. First, he cut up an old pizza box into long narrow strips and taped them together, end to end. Then he took one end of the strip and held it against the top edge of his refrigerator so that the trailing end reached the floor. He taped the top end into place, then dropped to his hands and knees and gently pulled the slack out of the dangling end. Using a pair of scissors he pulled from his back pocket, he cut the strip off where it touched the floor. "Yeah, good," he said. Carefully, he removed the cardboard strip from the refrigerator and rolled it into a disc, securing the trailing end with a piece of tape. Next, he repeated the process with a second strip of cardboard, this time across the bottom of the refrigerator.

Both discs he placed in his faux leather briefcase alongside a plastic drinking glass and an insert from the Sunday paper featuring advertisements for refrigerators and other kitchen appliances that would soon go on sale at the local Sears store. Lastly, he placed in his briefcase an envelope containing eight hundred dollars in cash, all in twenties. Eddie wasn't good with math, but he knew that five twenties equaled $100, and he had forty of them.

Satisfied that his preparations were complete, he called his friend for the third time that morning. "Pick me up," he said this time.

"I'm about to walk to the car," his friend said.

"Good."

Eddie took up his customary position by the front door, rocking forward and back in his usual manner, his feet firmly planted on the floor, one hand held to the back of his head, his gaze directed to the corner around which he knew his friend's car would appear.

Two months earlier, Eddie had been visiting his friend at his home. His new refrigerator immediately caught his eye. Unlike Eddie's, this one had the freezer on the bottom, not the top. And it had two French doors, one of which contained a dispenser for water and ice.

"Need new 'frigerator," Eddie said.

"Yours works fine."

"Need two doors. Freezer on bottom. Water and ice on front," Eddie said. "You buy."

The friend wasn't surprised by Eddie's interest in his refrigerator. He knew that he liked to keep abreast of the latest trends. When Eddie needed a microwave, he purchased the most expensive one available at the time. His first washer and dryer he replaced with a stackable set when he started seeing them displayed in the big box stores that he frequently visited on his Saturday morning walks.

"I'm not going to buy you a new refrigerator," the friend said. "Buy it yourself."

"No mimi," Eddie said. "Broke."

"Then start saving your money."

"How much?"

"I don't know. I bet you could find something for about $800."

"Lotta hundred dollars," Eddie said, feigning dejection.

"It *is* a lot of money," the friend said. "But you can do it. Use part of your income tax refund."

Eddie would do it; his friend could tell.

Although Eddie usually spent all of his money soon after he cashed his paycheck, he could save money when he put his mind to it. Within a month or two, he had saved the eight hundred dollars, in part by using his income tax refund and in part by selling his old refrigerator to the neighbor who, not coincidentally, had also purchased his old washer and dryer.

———

ON THE OTHER side of town, at the Sears store that once anchored Springfield, Ohio's preeminent mall but now remained one of the few establishments still open, the sales team waited with low expectations for customers that too seldom appeared. With nary a customer in the store, the new saleswoman leaned her butt against the sales counter, folded her arms across her chest, and stared into the distance, bored by the insipid banter emanating from the two salesmen who stood beside her. Already she was regretting her decision to make this her third job. Maybe she should have taken that waitressing job instead. Disgusted, she turned to her colleagues, interrupting them. "Where *is* everybody?" she demanded, as if they were to blame for the empty store. "I need to *sell* something."

"The third customer will be yours," one of the men replied. Both men laughed.

When Eddie and his friend arrived, Eddie jumped out of the car and walked as fast as he could into the store while his friend parked the car. Once inside, he looked around to get his bearings. Beyond the hardware section, he saw major appliances in the distance. He made a beeline for the three salespeople who were talking among themselves.

Unbeknownst to Eddie, he had been noticed as soon as he entered the store. All three watched as this short, thick-necked, round-faced, round-bellied man with thinning red hair broke into something resembling a trot, one hand holding the briefcase and the other holding up his pants. The salesman whose place in the pecking order dictated that Eddie would be his customer suddenly declined to take advantage of the opportunity. "You're the one who's so hot to sell something," he told the woman. "Here's your chance." Both men chuckled.

Reluctantly, the woman stepped forward.

"Hi girl!" Eddie exclaimed in the high-pitched voice that he used when he was excited.

"May I help you?" she asked perfunctorily, assuming that she couldn't.

Eddie placed his briefcase on the top of a nearby washing machine and extracted the advertising insert. Smoothing out the page across the lid, he pointed to the refrigerator that he wanted.

The woman led Eddie to the desired model. "Does that look like the one you want?"

Eddie held up the advertisement next to the refrigerator and compared it to the one in front of which he now stood. "Yeah, do," he said, nodding his head vigorously.

"It's on sale," she said. "For $750."

"Lotta hundred dollars," Eddie said, wide-eyed, suddenly feigning doubt.

When, at that moment, Eddie's friend arrived after parking his car, the woman's eyes registered a glimmer of hope. "Does he want to buy it?" she asked the friend.

The friend declined to respond, instead pointing his finger back at Eddie. Eddie could handle himself in these situations, he knew.

But Eddie had tests to run before making his buying decision. First, he pulled out the longer of the coiled strips of cardboard, removed the piece of tape, and held one end to the top of the refrigerator. "You hold," he said to the saleswoman.

The woman didn't understand.

"He wants you to hold on to the end of the cardboard strip," the friend said.

"Oh," she said, complying.

Eddie extended the strip down the length of the refrigerator. "Good, good," he said.

"What's good about it?" she asked.

"Not too tall."

The woman smiled.

Next, he unrolled the second coil of cardboard across the bottom of the refrigerator, this time requiring no assistance.

"Not too wide either?" the woman asked.

"Nope. Good."

The woman now watched with interest as Eddie extracted the drinking glass from his briefcase and placed it in the ice water slot on the front of the refrigerator. It fit. The woman laughed out loud.

"Buy now," he said.

"Great!" the woman said. Then she looked at Eddie's friend. "How does he plan...?" But she caught herself and returned her attention to Eddie. "How do *you* plan to pay for it?"

Eddie carefully laid out all of these twenty-dollar bills in eight rows of five each. "Lotta hundred dollars," he said.

"Yes, it is," she said, grateful for her good fortune. She was about to make a cash sale in less than ten minutes. She stole a glance at her still idle compatriots, relishing the regret that she saw written on their faces.

CHAPTER TWO

1968

Six-year-old Eddie Fugate reached up and batted at the latch that kept him confined to his crib. He liked the clickety-clack sound of the latch bouncing against the metal lid, so he did it again. But twice was enough, so he rolled onto his stomach, got up on his hands and knees, and pushed his butt against his ankles. Trying to dissipate the energy that always coursed through his body, he lunged forward and rocked back again and again. But when a shaft of sunlight appeared suddenly through a curtainless window, he shielded his eyes with one arm and, with the other, grabbed the rungs on the side of the crib, jostling the bed out of the sun's path. When the sun disappeared behind a cloud, he rolled back onto his stomach, got up on his hands and knees, and started rocking again.

On the other side of the bedroom wall, Eddie's mother watched absently as her youngest daughter huddled over her coloring book, thankful that the little girl's two older sisters had already left for school.

"Mommy," the little girl said without looking up. "Why does Eddie have to go away?"

"Because we can't take care of him anymore," the mother said, leaving unspoken her concern that Eddie's increasingly uncontrollable behavior was making their home unsafe for her three daughters and herself.

"Will he come back?"

"Maybe. When he's older. If he gets better." With her index finger, she traced the boundary of a scar on the surface of the old Formica-topped table, unaware that the circular motion of her finger coincided with the thump, thump, thump from the room next to her. Because she knew that the events of this day would haunt her for the rest of her life, she thought now only about the past. She recalled fondly the day when she left the hospital with her newborn son. "Let me push your wheelchair," an attendant had said. "Maybe it will be the last time anyone makes a fuss over you." And it was.

Two years later, first one doctor and then another told her that her son was mentally retarded, the second one adding that "he's probably not trainable. He has autism. He's autistic," he said again for emphasis, even though he knew that it was a seldom used term that she would not understand. "There are places he can go where he can be taken care of. It's something you should consider."

———

SINCE THEN, she had managed as best she could. She adapted to her son's constant activity by learning to live with as little sleep as he did. She forced herself to curb the urge to hug him when he became upset. And she learned to stay calm during his temper tantrums, understanding that the only thing she could do was to make them worse. But when he lashed out at one of his sisters during an especially violent episode, she determined that the doctor had been right. She knew then what she had to do, even if she didn't want to do it.

She walked to the bedroom and loosened the latch that held the lid in place. Back at the kitchen table, she watched and waited while her son busied himself with the little wooden automobile, the only toy from among a basketful that seemed to interest him. The knock at the door would come soon enough.

———

As the old judge stood at the window, absorbed in his thoughts, he welcomed the same sliver of the morning sun that had touched the boy in his crib. His three-piece tailored suit hung loosely on his diminished frame, and he looked vulnerable as he stood quietly in his chambers on the second floor of the nineteenth-century courthouse in downtown Cincinnati. Behind him, the social worker from Children's Services shifted her weight so that she roused the creaky hardwood floor to life. When still the judge did not acknowledge her, she cleared her throat too obviously.

"I'm sorry," said the judge, turning to look at her.

She directed his eyes to the file folder on his desk. "It's the Fugate case," she said.

But the judge made no move to examine the file. Unexpectedly, he engaged the woman in conversation.

"Ever hear of the Mello-Tones?"

"Sure."

"It's a children's choir," the judge said, oblivious to the

social worker's acknowledgment. "They sing two-part harmony, and they're all retarded. Every one of them."

"Yes, sir."

"And guess where they live."

"They live with their families," the social worker said, surprised that she was asked to state the obvious.

"Exactly. They live among us."

The judge sat down heavily as if, this time, he was the one on the receiving end of an indictment. Belatedly, he had come to realize that too seldom during the course of his career had he acted with the best interests of the child in mind. Instead, it was the protection of the community that had always been his foremost concern. By removing the former from the latter, he diminished both. He now understood. But while the judge today acted with a heavy heart, for Edward Fugate, the result would be the same. The judge opened the file and quickly scanned its contents. On the last page, he scrawled his name.

———

THE SOCIAL WORKER paused at the front door of the apartment, then knocked firmly. When the door opened, she followed the woman into the house and watched her return to her seat at the kitchen table. She noticed that the young boy sat on the old couch next to his sister, and she was struck by how much they looked alike. The boy wore brown corduroy pants and a blue-striped shirt. He was freshly scrubbed, and his thick red hair was still relaxed from the moisture that was in it.

Experience had taught the social worker to act quickly in these situations, and that is what she did. "This is for the best," she said as she took the young boy by the hand.

"I know," Mrs. Fugate said.

She and her daughter watched from the window as Eddie

walked to the waiting car. They would have been greatly comforted by the knowledge that this image of their son and brother would not be their last, but they had no way of knowing that.

Nor did they know of the special gifts Eddie possessed, not supernatural gifts, but everyday gifts possessed in super-abundance, gifts that Eddie would use to pursue the simplest of dreams—to be like everybody else, nothing more.

CHAPTER THREE

1974

Susan Armstrong's bottom hurt from bouncing along the two-lane country road on the hard seat of the old pickup truck. Her stomach was full of butterflies, and she was uncomfortable in her new "interview outfit," a pedestrian ensemble that was brought to life only by the beauty of its wearer. But her physical discomfort did not disturb a peace of mind borne of her assurance that, though she was not a religious person, she was going where she was called to go.

Why, then, was she suddenly uneasy? Finally, she became aware of the unmistakable beating noise of an approaching helicopter, and she wondered for an absurd instant if her husband might be aboard. She pulled the truck off the road, unwound her long legs from around the steering wheel, and slid off the seat. With one hand, she held her coat together at the neck. With the other, she shielded her eyes from the fine rain that lingered in the aftermath of killer tornadoes that only days before had wreaked havoc on the Midwest, leaving a swath of destruction across the city of Xenia, Ohio, just a few miles behind her.

According to news reports, Richard Nixon would today join Ohio's governor to inspect the damage. Thinking that the presidential party might now be overhead, she tried to catch a glimpse of the chopper, but the low ceiling prevented it. She was just as glad. Let the thing remain invisible in the cloud cover as it bore its damaged cargo toward ground zero so that the President of the United States, living in the death throes of Watergate and the shadow of impeachment, might again thrust his arms skyward in his famous gesture. Thus, he would give the residents of Xenia the courage to go on.

As the sound of the chopper faded in the distance, Susan thought again about her late husband, as she always did when she saw or heard a helicopter. After he entered the Army as one of the last to be drafted, he was sent to Vietnam, where he became one of the last soldiers to die in combat. She grieved deeply when she learned of her husband's death, but she put his loss behind her more quickly than she had expected. After a few months, she decided that she needed to get a job. That was what led her this day toward the Orient State Institute, southwest of Columbus.

Crossing into Pickaway County, she drove through gently rolling countryside that centuries before had been home to the Adena people, "mound builders" whose earthworks once dotted the landscape and one of which, a large earthen enclosure in the shape of a circle, had cradled the early settlement of Circleville, the county seat. Centuries later, here too were situated the Shawnee villages of the great chief Cornstalk, destroyed by Lord Dunmore in 1775 as part of his campaign to make the Ohio valley safe for Virginia's expansion. And in a farmer's field not far away once stood the famous Logan Elm beneath which Chief Logan delivered his oft-quoted lamentation.

But by the beginning of the twentieth century, a strange new people had arrived, and not by their own choosing. On land acquired by the State of Ohio in 1896 as a burying ground, construction began of the Custodial Farm, a branch of the Orient State Institute. By 1974, the number of residents exceeded 2,500, adults and children of both sexes.

In the little town of Orient, an obscure station on the Baltimore and Ohio Railroad and the source from which the institution took its name, Susan turned left and crossed over Big Darby Creek on an ancient truss bridge, its elegant finials now rusted but still intact. She followed the narrow road as it ascended a hill, the ground rising to her left and falling away on the right. Leaning forward to wipe condensation from the inside of the windshield, she hunched over the steering wheel as the road disappeared into a sulfurous haze that descended upon the valley whenever atmospheric conditions were such that smoke from the coal-burning power plant could not escape.

Aware of no sound other than the sloshing of the tires over the damp pavement, she slowed when she detected movement amidst the fog that was densest on the downhill side of the road. Approaching cautiously, she stepped hard on the brakes as a gray-haired man wearing bib overalls stepped forth from the shadows. Positioning himself squarely in front of the truck, he held menacingly in one hand a piece of wood.

Susan took her hands off the wheel and sat back in her seat, put off both by the man's threatening stance and his exaggerated buck teeth that made it impossible to fully contain the tobacco juice which streamed from the corner of his mouth and traveled in an oily rivulet onto his overalls.

"Dollah, wut," the man exclaimed as he walked around to the side of the truck, then opened the door.

Susan took her hands off the wheel and shrank back in her seat.

"Dollah, wut," the man said again through a stream of tobacco juice.

"Dollah wut?" Susan asked, dumbfounded.

But when two more odd-looking men appeared, she relaxed. The presence of one strange man was hard to interpret, but not three. She guessed that they were residents of the institution.

The men deposited their wood in the truck and returned to the shadows from which they emerged moments later with large armfuls, which they also put in the truck.

"Dollah," the man said.

Finally, Susan understood. She had just purchased a load of firewood for the agreed-upon price of one dollar. Relieved, she extracted a dollar from her purse.

When the men retreated backward to await the next customer, Susan drove on up the hill toward the dozens of mostly brick buildings. Not knowing where the employment office was, she parked in front of the Administration Building, hoping that the strange-looking little man descending the steps would be able to help her.

The man saw her, too, and positioned himself so that he could greet the pretty lady behind the wheel. But when Susan briefly and inadvertently exposed a shapely leg as she climbed out of the truck, his attention was momentarily diverted so that he was not the one who initiated the conversation.

"Can you tell me where the employment office is?" Susan asked.

The man pointed behind him to the Administration Building without turning around to look at it. "My work," he said in a flat monotone that sounded like a record played on a turntable that wasn't turning fast enough.

"What do you do there?"

"Working boy."

She decided not to ask him what the work was that a working boy performed, so she asked him his name.

"Otto," he said.

At any other time, Otto would have been interested in a longer conversation, but he was on his way to the dining hall, so he got to the reason why he was interested in Susan's arrival in the first place. "Gimme a dollar," he said.

Susan produced yet another dollar, which Otto stuffed into his pocket. Later she would learn that after Otto graduated from high school, he was sent to Orient when his mother decided to remarry, reluctantly acceding to a longstanding precondition that she gets rid of her intellectually impaired son. Because Otto knew how to read and write, he advanced quickly through the ward system to become a working boy. Although most working boys were assigned to the barns and fields, Otto worked in the personnel office, where he filed and performed other clerical work.

She watched Otto as he ambled off, then she lifted her eyes and looked out over the valley, taking a rough inventory of what she saw. Scores of large red brick buildings were arrayed across the hillside: barns, service buildings, and a dozen or more "cottages" falling away in all directions. In the distance, the Big Darby Creek meandered serenely, then hooked back to gather the rich bottom lands farmed by residents of the institution. Closer in, tractors struggled against pieces of farm machinery, and groups of men moved from one chore to the next. More working boys, she assumed. But something else loomed amidst the bustle of daily activity. It was, she finally realized, the unseen but palpable presence of those who remained inside. *How many could there be? She wondered. From the size of the place, there must be thousands!*

CHAPTER FOUR

B ecause the small group of staff members intended to stay outside only long enough to conclude the brief ceremony for which they had been recruited, they gathered near the door in the horseshoe-shaped space created by the intersection of two wings with the long main building. All of this was part of Cottage A, so named because it stood first in a line that extended away from the Administration Building.

The group had assembled at the invitation of Annabelle Atkins, who was the last to arrive. Plainly dressed, with her hair pulled tightly into a bun, she greeted her coworkers with only a nod and the thinnest of smiles. But her austerity belied a kindness that was apparent even to the unobservant. Occupying the euphemistically titled position of Hospital Aide, Annabelle was like many of the "hillbilly mamas" who came to work at Orient, if perhaps from a background that was more humble than most. Born into poverty, she went shoeless until she entered school and didn't brush her teeth until the school nurse told her that it was something she should do every day.

When Annabelle discovered that the group had assembled on the side away from the rising sun, she motioned for the half-dozen women to follow her as she walked further away from the building toward the warmth beyond the shadows. As the group moved into the sun, they escaped more than the cold. Inadvertently, they moved beyond the force field of the institution–beyond the hurly-burly of the wards, beyond the jangle of music that blared from competing radios, beyond the inarticulate ravings of residents whose unfathomable declamations were too rarely recognized as the eloquence of the abandoned. And finally, they moved beyond the pervasive stench, the lingering, ubiquitous amalgam of sweat and urine and grease to which one at some point became desensitized, recognizing it only by its absence.

When Annabelle felt the sun's warmth on her shoulders, she glanced heavenward to its source in the ice-blue cloudless sky that was at once both dense and empty and as awesome as the sun itself. She closed her eyes and breathed deeply, recognizing amid the gentle rustling of young leaves the distant call of a cardinal to its mate, everyday sounds that complemented and emphasized a natural order in stark contrast to the relentless regimentation and depersonalization that affected all of them to one extent or another.

Her attention was returned to the task at hand by the exclamation of a coworker. "Here he comes!"

Annabelle spread her arms and gathered her flock around the shiny new bicycle, shielding it from view. Pleased to see that, for once, the young lad was following instructions, she watched as he approached and saw him break into a run when he determined that the group was hiding something.

"Happy Birthday," the group shouted as one.

Twelve-year-old Eddie Fugate jumped on the bicycle as soon as he saw it. While the others struggled briefly to hold on to an arm or a leg or part of the bike, Annabelle gave him the only instruction he would receive.

"Be careful!" she shouted.

With no acknowledgment other than the smile on his face, Eddie Fugate zigzagged off into the distance.

"And stay away from the working boys," Annabelle added.

That got more to the crux of the thing. Maybe now he would stop commandeering the big three-wheelers that the working boys used to deliver mail and supplies to the cottages.

Eddie pedaled down Collins Lane without looking back. "Donk, donk, donk," he shouted, as he pedaled past sprawling brick cottages identified only by a letter (Cottages A, through H, but no G), past cottages named for trees (Elm and Maple), then past Morningside and Sunnyside, imposing but decaying three-story structures that housed non-ambulatory residents who rarely experienced either the morning or the sun. But when he spotted a group of women outside White Cottage, he pointed his bike at the big wooden gliders in which they sat two abreast and across from each other, each cradling a battered doll. He laughed out loud when he saw them stop rocking and clutch their babies to their breasts. Veering off at the last possible moment, he turned around and watched as they screamed with delight.

He spotted next a group of working boys loading dirty laundry onto a truck, and he rode for the middle of the pack. "Donk, donk, donk!" he shouted again as men dove in all directions, soiled sheets billowing behind them.

For the first time in his life, Eddie had an outlet for all of his energy. Leaning out over the bike with his butt and elbows held aloft and his head low over the handlebars, he flew by the new hospital, then headed for the barns, some still used for the purpose for which they were constructed, others converted to meet modern-day needs. He rode by the big brick horse barn, the swine barns, and the dairy barns. He pedaled through the middle of the big firehose house, now used to store farm machinery. Then he circled back around the power plant and turned down the dirt road that led to the fields, pedaling further and further away from the institution. By the time he reached the muddy waters of the Big Darby, he was breathing heavily and perspiring freely. Dismounting, he let his bike plop to the ground and walked to the edge of the creek.

There he stood. He didn't throw rocks. He didn't kick dirt in the water. He didn't reach for an overhanging limb. He just stood there. He listened to the gentle, barely audible gurgle of the water moving through the creek bed. He watched water bugs dance across its surface. He followed the progress of a stick as it floated slowly by. He bathed in the quiet. And he stood still for the longest time that he had ever stood still in his life.

CHAPTER FIVE

Annabelle pushed an escaped strand of hair back into her bun and watched as the first signs of agitation rippled through the group of men who stood along the dayroom wall. The wisdom gained from working on the wards for almost thirty years equipped her to handle almost any situation, including this one.

Several men rocked back and forth. One poked the man standing next to him while another picked at a large mole on his arm until blood seeped from the edges. If few among the group could distinguish the big hand from the little, they nonetheless possessed a collective awareness of the time of day that was precise to the minute, especially when it was time to go to the dining hall.

"Y'all ain't goin' no-wheres til ever-body's here," Annabelle said, then turned and yelled down the length of the ward toward the new aide. "How ya'll doin' down there?" When the question went unanswered, she moved casually down the line of men, patting some on the back, ignoring others.

Everyone wore the same one-size-fits-all cotton hospital

gown, or they wore nothing at all. Even so, the vast differences in appearance created a bizarre diversity. A few were quite young, while others were in their sixties. Most were white, but some were Black. Some were toilet trained, and many were not. While most were thought to be violent, some actually were. This was Ward 5, home of the "low grades."

"Now stay calm," Annabelle said. "The dinner bell will be a ringin' soon enough."

At the other end of the ward, the new aide was struggling with an uncooperative young man whose bulk marked him as one of the "fat boys." Today, as on several previous days, his aversion to wearing a gown was preventing him from doing the one thing that he liked to do more than anything else, namely eating.

"Owee," Susan screamed, almost to herself so as not to agitate the others. "You bit me, Pauly!"

Because Pauly was a biter, all of his teeth had been removed by the Orient dentist, but he could still hurt you, even with his gums.

Susan massaged the welt on her arm, then looked up to locate a second young man everyone called "the boxer." He wasn't a boxer, but he spent most days bent forward in a boxer's crouch, pawing the air with clenched fists. The boxer was without speech and communicated only his most basic needs, as he was doing now, tapping vigorously on his wrist where a wristwatch might be worn.

"We'll go in a minute," Susan said before returning her attention to Pauly, who sat sprawled on the floor, naked except for one canvas shoe. "You know the rules, Pauly. You can't go to the dining hall naked."

Susan handed Pauly a clean cotton gown that she had pulled from one of the big laundry bags delivered weekly to the ward in exchange for one with soiled gowns. "It's up to you, Pauly. If you wanna eat tonight, you gotta wear a gown."

He bit her again, this time on the ankle.

"Ouch!" she screamed. "Then it's no supper for Pauly."

That was too much for Annabelle. "I'm on my way," she said.

"No, don't!" Susan said, holding up her hand. "I can handle this."

The only question was how. Susan was mad at Pauly, and she was mad at herself. Unable to think what else to do, she resigned herself to Annabelle's intervention—yet again. Plopping down on the floor, she buried her face in her hands. Instantly, she became aware of two thoughts. This was no way to behave. And someone other than Annabelle was staring at her. She looked up to see Pauly looking at her with concern written across his face.

Pull yourself together, woman! He seemed to be saying, not with his mouth but with his eyes and with the sideways tilt of his head. *Pull yourself together for your sake and for mine.*

Susan smiled, getting the message. "I guess we're both having a bad day, aren't we, Pauly," she said, tugging on his earlobe and gently massaging his neck.

Pauly picked up a shoe and handed it to her.

"Are you hungry, Pauly?"

Pauly nodded and reached for the gown while Susan got to her feet and retrieved a nearby Geri chair, Pauly's usual mode of transportation.

"Then let's go eat."

Pauly lowered himself into the chair and propelled the chair forward with shuffling feet. When Annabelle opened the big steel door, the men moved as a group down the hallway. Most walked quickly but awkwardly while some shuffled, some limped, and one or two rode in Geri chairs pushed by others.

Inside the dining hall, the men slid onto steel benches attached to steel tables. Each table was preset with individual trays of food, the identity of which was hard to determine since it had been mashed and ground to accommodate those, like Pauly, who was unable to chew. *Kind of smells like it might be lasagna,* Susan thought as she moved among the tables, making sure that everyone took nourishment and that no one was "thieven'," particularly the fat boys, many of whom could inhale an entire plate of food in one giant gulp.

Some men used spoons (no knives or forks for low grades), but most ate with their hands. Pauly had his own system. First, he drank his milk, then he poured his salad into the empty container and drank that. Finally, he drank his lasagna, if that's what it was. Like everyone else, Pauly ate quickly.

At the back of the room, the young redheaded boy slipped in the door without being noticed, or so he thought. After quickly surveying the room, he walked to a nearby closet which, though usually locked like everything else at the institution, now swung open, its contents in use by the aides. His eyes went immediately to the wooden shelves. Finding the first one held in place only by gravity, he lifted the board off of its slats. He removed another in the same fashion, then walked toward the door with one board under each arm. But the load was too heavy, so he dropped one board and left with the other. When he returned for the second, he discovered too late that his path was obstructed. The collision knocked him on his butt. When he looked up, he saw standing above him a very tall blonde-headed woman.

"Hello," Susan said, bending down to help him up.

Eddie scrambled away, not because he feared the repercussions of having been caught stealing, but because he had, without warning, found himself next to a human being who, as far as he could tell, might very well want to hug him.

Susan stepped back. "Hello," she said again.

The boy jumped to his feet. He looked at Susan, then he looked at the board. Confident that she wouldn't stop him, he picked up the board and left.

CHAPTER SIX

Susan passed by the employee entrance at the front of the building, then turned a corner to reach the courtyard between Wards 3 and 4, the same courtyard in which Eddie collected his new bicycle. She hurried to her accustomed seat on a bench, ignoring the hot summer sun, which, together with the humidity, made this an uncomfortable place to spend the few minutes that remained before her shift started. She hadn't missed much, she decided, lighting a cigarette. A few months ago, she was only a dabbler, but now she was an addict, seduced by the culture of the institution in which the use of tobacco was widespread among staff and residents alike, except for those low grades who couldn't handle it and whose access was therefore restricted.

When she heard a sound that put her in mind of newlyweds dragging a string of tin cans behind their car, she looked up to see Eddie pedaling toward her, several pieces of lumber and other odds and ends clattering along on a rope tied to the back of his bike. She watched as he skidded to a stop, jumped off, and untied the items.

Susan had tried to get close to the boy ever since their encounter in the dining hall, but he moved so fast and so unpredictably that it was hard to find him. She knew where to find him in the evening. He would be in his crib in the dormitory on Ward 3 with the rest of the boys, ages six and up. Whenever she visited, she stood where he couldn't see her. He was always awake, usually rocking furiously.

She also knew where to find him earlier in the day. He was in school, thanks to a recent Supreme Court decision that held that everyone had a right to an education. But when she reported to work in the afternoon, school was over. So before every shift and during every break, she walked the grounds hoping for a chance encounter, then stopped at the bench where she was sitting now.

She watched as Eddie dragged a piece of plywood closer to the crude wooden hut that put her in mind of an igloo. Constructed from scrap lumber, Eddie had nailed asphalt shingles to the sides but not to the roof. Susan marveled at the totality of his concentration as he busied himself with his next task. She saw it in his eyes and heard it in the machine-like sound that emanated from a point deep within him, a sound that, for the rest of his life, would signal a man consumed by his work. But the noise stopped when he picked up the piece of the plywood, crawled through the opening, and dragged it in after him.

Must be the floor, Susan thought.

When Eddie emerged, Susan assumed that he was done for the day. But instead of mounting his bicycle, he wheeled it over to the building and placed it inside. What he did next brought Susan to her feet. He took two or three steps toward her and looked her in the eye.

"Donk," Eddie said. "Donk haw."

Not understanding, Susan scrunched up her shoulders and held out her hands, palms upward.

"Donk," Eddie said again, pointing first to the bicycle and then to the building. "Donk haw."

At last, she got it. A "donk" was a bicycle, and Eddie had built a house for it, a "donk haw." The first words that Eddie spoke to another human being, he spoke to her.

———

THE NEXT NIGHT, after a difficult shift, Susan collapsed into one of the big wooden rocking chairs in the ward where she worked. She didn't see Eddie when he approached, but when he slid onto her lap and placed his head against her breast, he injected himself into her consciousness in a way that instantly engaged all her senses. She said nothing but continued to rock gently, making no effort to alter the embrace that she had naturally assumed. She was surprised at how thin he was and how light he was, and she half expected him to float away. Feeling as if a butterfly had landed, she urgently and indelibly recorded what she saw in case this visit was his last. She looked closely at the freckles on his cheeks and arms. She took note of the dirt under his fingernails and examined the fresh scratch on his leg. She brushed gently at the dust that clung to his tennis shoes. She breathed deeply and captured his scent. And when she sensed that their encounter was nearing its end, she whispered into his ear. "Thank you," she said.

The bond between them was now unbreakable.

CHAPTER SEVEN

Tony Marino jumped between the two youths and pried them apart. "We don't hit people," he said.

The stocky teenager everyone called Tank was usually the aggressor, but this time he was provoked by another teenager who now stood standing just out of reach. Cackling happily, the instigator pushed his protective helmet up on his forehead, then repeated the gesture that had started the fracas in the first place. He raised his hand in front of his face with three fingers held up in a way that approximated the letter "W." Because he lacked the dexterity that would permit him to isolate the middle digit, this was his unique version of the universally recognized obscene gesture.

Tank lunged again, and Tony pushed him away while, at the same time, he pulled the other boy's arm down. "Knock it off," he said.

Tony Marino was one of about three-dozen teachers hired to provide instruction to a group known as the "trainable mentally retarded." Since most of the teachers who had come before him had already quit, some after only a few hours on

the job, he was employed on the spot and awarded a "Temporary T.M.R. certificate." The personnel officer's passing
comment constituted the only direction he ever received.
"Anything you can do for those people will be appreciated," he
had said, leaving Tony to find his own way to Maple Cottage,
the cottage to which he had been assigned according to the
paper that was thrust into his hand. Given no textbooks, no
classroom, and no students, Tony followed his instincts. An
unused room in the basement became his classroom, and the
eight boys and girls he recruited from nearby cottages became
his first students.

The youngest son of European immigrants, Tony was
raised in a tough neighborhood in East Cleveland near the area
known as Little Italy. Although he was a good student, Tony
would always believe that his real education was earned on the
streets amid the wailing sirens, domestic arguments, and petty
crimes that were everyday occurrences. Later, he would come
to appreciate that, while he had witnessed the ravages of
poverty and the onset of social disintegration, he was lucky to
be among the last children raised in the era before guns and
drugs came to dominate daily life.

On his first day in high school, the wrestling coach picked
him out of a crowd and encouraged him to come out for the
team. While it was true that he recognized in Tony the qualities of both a competitor and a leader, he also knew that the
team needed someone to wrestle in the 138-pound weight
class. Tony improved every year, earning all-state honors when
he was a senior, an accomplishment that he parlayed into a
partial scholarship to Ohio State, where he majored in
anthropology.

After he graduated and lost his deferment, he joined the
Navy rather than allow himself to be drafted. But instead of sea
duty, he was trained as a firefighter and assigned to a seldom-

used airstrip on the Naval Base in Guantanamo Bay, Cuba, where he and the rest of the crew trained vigilantly for a plane crash they hoped would never occur. Separated from most of his peers by education and attitude, his days drew out into a comfortable sameness. Early each morning, he bypassed the enlisted mess in favor of a nearly abandoned airport café incongruously presided over by an ancient Chinaman who, upon preparing the eggs and sausage that Tony always ordered, quickly retreated into the shadows and his own life of isolation. When Tony got off duty, he ran for miles along the airstrip in the hot afternoon sun, then adjourned to the EM club to drink twenty-cent beers and listen a thousand times to Simon and Garfunkel sing *Cecilia*. In the evening, he watched old Randolph Scott westerns at one of the free outdoor theaters and read in week-old news magazines the accounts of Woodstock and Mylai and Kent State. Both by choice and circumstance, he lived a life of desultory solitude, thankful to be in a safe place, yet vaguely uneasy because he thought that all he was doing was killing time. But although he was not tested by combat, he nonetheless absorbed sufficient wisdom from the experience so that by the time he returned to the States, he had learned how to be an adult. Three years later and armed with an honorable discharge, he bought an old car and drove to Columbus to visit friends and look for a job.

Tony and his colleagues were hired not as part of a grand plan to reform Orient but as a preliminary and inadequate response to the public's growing awareness of the living conditions in state institutions, and not just in Ohio. In the wake of reports like the one filed by Geraldo Rivera two years before when he exposed the wretched conditions at Willowbrook State School in New York, incidents that previously drew no attention were now reported.

Increasingly aggressive advocates added to the pressure for

change. Only months before, in a landmark case that would reach the U.S. Supreme Court, lawyers filed suit on behalf of residents at the Pennhurst State School and Hospital near Philadelphia. Citing "unsanitary, inhuman, and dangerous" conditions, they sought an order that the institution be closed. At the same time, Congress had under consideration the Education of Handicapped Children Act, legislation precipitated in part by the realization that more than one million handicapped children received no educational instruction. Belatedly, officials at Orient prepared for change. They did so in part by creating the program through which Tony was hired.

"Listen to me now," Tony said to the two combatants. He spoke calmly, continuing to hold both boys apart. "No hitting is the rule for all of us." Tony rotated his head in a circular motion to indicate that he was including the other six students who were also in the room and who, for the moment, were enjoying the spectacle.

Dealing with behavior problems was Tony's specialty. The two young men involved in this dispute had been in his class for several weeks. Although Tony had experienced nothing more serious than the clumsy scuffle that he was now breaking up, he knew that their former teacher was relieved to be rid of both of them, especially Tank, who was shunned by staff and residents alike for the obsession that would increasingly define him as a low-grade.

Tank was a "window breaker." Because of him and others like him, the glass in many of the windows had been replaced by Plexiglas or sometimes with a piece of plywood. Tank liked everything about breaking glass. He liked the sound that glass made when it splintered on the hard terrazzo. He liked the fragility that he sensed so fleetingly during the instant that his knuckles made contact with the brittle surface. He liked the riskiness of an act that, for the less accomplished practitioner, sometimes resulted in serious injury. And he liked the aftermath when, for an instant, all other activity ceased, and attention was directed at him. Because he knew that the resulting mess would be cleaned up by someone else, he always delivered a blow that cast the shards in the widest possible arc. But when his purpose was to escape the oppressiveness of the ward, he inflicted upon himself an injury of sufficient severity to ensure a trip to the infirmary, knowing that his lacerations would be attended by a nurse who would treat him like a human being.

The other youth, known as Junior because he was named after his father, or so it was assumed, was the more typical adolescent, continually seeking the approval of his peers, which he earned by performing a service that provided much entertainment. When in the distance the sound of a siren was first discerned, every child who was able rushed to the window in anticipation then clapped and laughed and pointed when the big, noisy, red fire truck came into view. In the midst of the commotion was Junior. This was his doing. Junior was a fire alarm puller.

Tony discovered that the need for physical intervention occurred most frequently during the days immediately following the assignment to his class. Once the student learned the rules, the need diminished. Cooperation and hard work were rewarded by granting opportunities to listen to the radio or play an album on the record player. On those occasions when Tony wanted to reward the whole class, he took everyone down to the Big Darby to fish for carp, an experience that, in the beginning, was as new for him as it was for his students. But the prize that was most cherished was a trip to the Commissary.

A place by custom open to staff and residents alike, the Commissary was a one-story brick building located across the street from Kirk School where the approximately two hundred "educable mentally retarded" children attended classes. Outside the Commissary, knots of people shared a last piece of gossip before their shift started, lingering among the clumps of three-wheeled bikes used by the working boys. Inside, residents conversed with staff as they stood together in the same cafeteria-style line or sat at the same tables consuming ham hocks and beans, eggs and grits, or biscuits and gravy.

But in the basement of Maple Cottage, no one contemplated a trip to the Commissary.

"You know what comes next, Tank," Tony said. "If you don't sit down, I'll have to take you down."

Although Tank ignored Tony, Junior extricated himself and joined Stevie, a young lad with Down Syndrome, on the white wooden bench that Tony had taken from one of the day rooms.

"Tank, bam!" Stevie said in anticipation of the action that he hoped might occur.

Stevie was Tony's favorite student. Several weeks before, Tony had taken Stevie for an eye exam to see if the doctor could prescribe something to keep the gunk from collecting in the lower corners of his eyes. Instead, the doctor fitted him with glasses and told Tony to clean his eyes every morning, instructions which Tony followed faithfully.

"Here goes, Tank. I'm going to take you down," Tony said when Tank directed his aggressiveness toward Tony now that Junior was on the sidelines.

In one motion, Tony grabbed him by the shoulders and pushed him back and over his outstretched leg, forcing Tank down, but not too roughly. Then, using the technique that the wrestling coach had drilled into him years before, he made sure that Tank stayed down. "Your opponent is like a table," the coach used to say. "You've got to remove the legs."

After a few moments, Tank relaxed.

"I'm going to slide off of you, Tank, but you just stay where you are."

Tony moved aside, and Tank rolled over onto his back but made no effort to get up. The crisis had passed.

"What do I always say at a time like this?" Tony asked the whole group.

"Don't hurt somebody," Stevie offered.

"Right, Stevie. Thank you! It's okay to get mad. It's okay to feel angry. But you can't hurt other people."

Tony patted Tank on the shoulder, and they both got up. To Tony's surprise, Tank offered to shake Junior's hand. It was another one of those taken-for-granted conventions that Tony had been trying to teach his students until now, without success in Tank's case. After they shook hands, they both smiled. Then there were handshakes all around.

"I think this calls for a trip to the Commissary," Tony said amid much jubilation.

CHAPTER EIGHT

Although trips to the Commissary had become an effective tool for behavior management, Tony was starting to feel the effects in his pocketbook. "One item only," he said to Junior, who was standing in front of him with an empty bottle raised in the air.

Junior tossed the empty into the trash bin, then hurried back outside so he could climb on and off one of the three-wheeled bikes that were left unattended while the working boy that was using it dined inside. When Tony saw him leave, he went outside to check on him, and Stevie followed.

"You can sit on it, Junior. But don't ride it," Tony said. "They're for official business only."

Once Tony was sure his orders were being followed, he leaned against the commissary wall and relaxed. When he did, his attention was drawn again to the banner that hung from the second-floor window of Kirk School across the street. A single word was emblazoned in tall black letters:

HUMANIZATION

Tony chuckled softly, appreciating the irony of an admonition that was seen and read by the occasional visitor but was no longer noticed by the staff for whom it was intended. Lest they forget, they were now expected to treat human beings like human beings, a change so alien to Orient's culture that its implementation required a campaign. Was the humanization campaign underway at all the institutions in the state? Tony assumed that it was.

When Tony realized that Stevie was standing beside him, leaning against the wall in the same manner as he was—with his hands in his pockets, his butt against the red bricks, the idle leg crossed over the top of the one that bore most of his weight—he was pleased and amused. To return the compliment, he pushed his own tongue out over his lower lip like Stevie's tongue was now, and like it was much of the time, for that matter. Then, playfully raising the stakes, Tony put his finger in his ear. Stevie smiled and did likewise, then put his free hand on top of his head. Tony followed suit, and they both laughed as they stood holding their ridiculous positions, seeing who would falter first.

Tony didn't see the little redheaded kid when he came around the corner, but when the kid brushed against his legs so that he almost lost his balance, Tony thought that he might have done it on purpose. Tony's feet slid further from the wall, but he remained upright, and he and Stevie both laughed again. But in the next instant, they both fell silent, stunned by the sudden presence of the stranger who appeared from the same direction as the little redhead.

In slow-motion amazement, Stevie dropped his hands, swallowed hard, and struggled to stand up. Tony was slower to react. As he stood frozen with his legs crossed, a hand atop his head, and a finger sticking in his ear, he thought to himself that this was the most beautiful woman he had ever seen.

Maybe the tallest, too, he thought from his diminished position.

Susan was no less fascinated. Everything about the man in front of her reinforced the friendly laugh that she had heard before she came around the corner. She liked his smile, which showed lots of teeth. She liked his dark brown eyes that were framed nicely by his angular face. She liked that he seemed different. A vaguely urban look, she decided. And the bond that she sensed between Stevie and Tony magnified his appeal.

With some effort, Tony uncrossed his legs and inched himself up the wall without lowering his hands. Then he extracted his finger from his ear as if it were stuck. In the same manner, he removed the hand from atop his head. "Howdy, Ma'am," he said, touching the brim of an imaginary hat. "They call me Tony, and this here's my sidekick, Stevie," he said, pointing with his thumb.

"Hello, Stevie," Susan replied, extending her hand. Although she was still engaged in the act of shaking Stevie's small hand, her gaze returned to Tony. "My name is Susan."

"You must be new around these here parts," Tony said, maintaining his cowboy persona.

"I work second shift."

"But this is first shift."

"Then I must not be working," Susan said. But she thought her retort sounded smart-alecky, so she hurried to correct the impression. "Sometimes, I come in early to visit with Eddie and keep an eye on him."

She had forgotten about Eddie! She looked around quickly, then relaxed when she spotted him nearby, observing the group at a distance. "That's Eddie over there," she said, pointing.

"Why isn't he in school?"

Now it was Tony who was mad at himself. He sounded like a truant officer.

"He went to Kirk School for a while," Susan said, nodding toward the building across the street. "But he got thrown out."

"What did he do?"

"One day, he turned all the ovens in the home economics room up to 500 degrees. All the little cakes got burned up."

Tony laughed, and so did Stevie.

"They had to call the fire department."

"I know some people who would have liked to have been there to see that," Tony said.

"I'm surprised you didn't hear about it."

Tony sensed an opportunity. "You mean he's not in anyone's class now?"

"Not right now."

"Maybe he'd like to be in mine," Tony said.

"Maybe he would."

Just like that, Eddie became the youngest child in Tony's class and one of the youngest in the T.M.R. program.

But as Eddie moved off and Susan followed him, she was surprised and perplexed by the odd notion that kept running through her head. "I'll never be able to wear high heels," she thought to herself. It was a peculiar thought for a woman who could not remember a time when she wore any shoe that made her seem taller than she already was.

CHAPTER NINE

As was true for all the alphabetically named cottages, the residents of Cottage A slept in two large dormitories in the basement. In the morning, after everyone arose, the single sheet and the cotton blanket were removed from each bed and stuffed into a large laundry bag hung on a metal frame. The higher-functioning guys from the first and second wards and some of the children in Ward 3 performed this task themselves, but many of the lower-functioning men from Ward 4 and Ward 5 needed help. Because collecting the bedding was a low-skilled and often smelly job, a group of working boys assisted, using broom handles to remove the sheets and blankets that were badly soiled, then carrying the full bags to the laundry room in a nearby building.

Because Susan worked the second shift, these tasks were completed by the time she arrived for work in mid-afternoon. By four o'clock on most days, she was accompanying the guys to the dining hall, starting with the working boys in Ward 1 and finishing with the "kids in the back," meaning the men in Ward 4 and Ward 5 who ate last. After supper, she would help move everyone to the showers where on some days, she helped men undress, and on other days she manned a hose with a showerhead attached to it. Then she would go with guys to the dormitories, or she would stay behind to clean the bathrooms. Using ample quantities of disinfectant, all exposed surfaces would be mopped and hosed down, a task facilitated by the lack of toilet stalls and toilet seats, the porcelain "hoppers," as they were called, protruding from the concrete floor in a long row down the length of the room.

But today, for Susan, all of these tasks remained in the future. Arriving early for work as she so often did, this time she went directly to the laundry room to talk to Goldie, an ancient wisp of a woman who presided over the room from her perch in a large rocking chair just inside the door. When Goldie barely acknowledged Susan's deliberately cheerful greeting, Susan got right to the point. "I got something I want to show you, Goldie," she said.

"What?" Goldie asked, looking up from the sock she was darning, an important part of her job when she first started to work at Orient, but now just something that she did to pass the time.

"I bought some new clothes for Eddie Fugate," Susan said, removing several shirts and pairs of pants from a shopping bag and holding them within Goldie's line of vision. "Do you know who I'm talking about?"

"Nope."

"He's a cute little redhead. He's twelve, but he looks more like he's eight or nine."

"I know who you mean," Goldie said. "I seen him around."

"I'm hoping that you can help me make sure these clothes don't get mixed in with the ones that all of the other boys wear."

Susan knew that a few parents, when they visited, sometimes brought new clothing for their children. But she also knew that if the child ever wore the clothes again after it was washed for the first time, it was just luck.

"Ain't no need to keep his duds separate," Goldie said. "Ain't nobody else small enough to wear 'em no-ways."

"Of course!" Susan exclaimed. "I can't believe I didn't think of that."

Her concern was allayed, and Susan hurried off to do one last thing before she started her shift. She knew that it was only a matter of time until Eddie's donk house was deemed a hazard or an eyesore or some such thing. A quick inspection of the building site confirmed that her suspicions were well founded. The donk house was gone, apparently removed by the maintenance crew. But she saw that a new donk house was already rising in its place. The momentary apprehension that she felt when she discovered Eddie's new project was replaced by a flutter of anticipation. She had a good reason to go see Tony, not that she really needed one.

She was dismayed to find Tony's classroom empty, and she started to leave, but then she heard the voices of approaching children, and she took a seat in the back of the room. Tony was the last one to enter, and for a moment, he didn't see her, occupied as he was with the stragglers, one of whom was Stevie.

"Hello," she said.

"Hello," Tony said, surprised but pleased. Then he turned to his children, who were dirty and sweaty but very happy. "Did we have fun today?"

After a chorus of affirmatives, Tony shooed them off to their cottages.

"Big outing today?" Susan asked.

"Yep. We went to the summer festival down at Commercial Point," Tony said, referring to the annual carnival in the village down the road. "We're going camping in a couple of weeks. Maybe you'd like to go with us."

"Maybe I would," Susan said. "But I've never been before. Does that make a difference?"

"Nope. You've given me fair warning," Tony said. "Did you bring me a present?" he asked, nodding at the bag in Susan's hand.

"No. These are new clothes for Eddie."

"Darn. But then, I guess you don't really know me well enough yet to be giving me presents, do you?"

"I don't."

"We should work on changing that."

"We should."

"Is that why you came to see me?"

"No. I need a favor. Eddie built another... garage," she said, finding the right word.

"That's not good. Eddie's starting to make quite a name for himself."

"I'm hoping you can tear it down," Susan said. "So that Eddie doesn't get in trouble. It's small, more like a lean-to than a house. It's just big enough to hold his bike."

"If you take his bike, I'll tear it down."

"If he builds another one, will you tear it down too?"

"I will if you come and get me."

"You could just check for yourself to see if he built one."

"I could, except I probably couldn't find it."

"It would probably be in the same place."

"I would get lost. I have a terrible sense of direction."

So several times a week, Susan went to Tony's class, sometimes to report the existence of a new donk house and sometimes just to visit.

CHAPTER TEN

Cottage A was one of the many crumbling structures built in the 1920s, largely with funding from the state of Ohio. But the adoption of the Medicare and Medicaid amendments to the Social Security Act meant that institutions like Orient would be eligible for significant federal funding if they could meet costly new standards. As a result, construction was underway on several new, state-of-the-art nursing home-like facilities.

These new construction projects quickly captured Eddie's attention. There were people who knew what they were doing. They possessed materials and tools, and skills that he had never seen before. He spent many satisfying hours on the perimeter of the various sites, just watching and learning. On weekends when work stopped, he returned to the sites to pilfer materials for the donk house on which he was working at the moment.

During the week, when he was done with school, and he wasn't working on his donk house, he looked for other opportunities to entertain himself. The obvious targets were the occupants of the buildings on either side of Cottage A: a large two-story brick building called Doren Hall on one side and the Administration Building on the other. He quickly ruled out Doren Hall since it was occupied entirely by working boys. He'd had enough encounters with working boys to know that this was not a group he wanted to antagonize.

The Administration Building and the people in it, on the other hand, were a source of longstanding fascination. Eddie knew that on occasion, a person from the big building, often wearing a white shirt and tie, would come to his cottage and take one of his fellow residents back for a "meeting," as Susan would later explain. And he knew that once or twice, the resident never returned. He knew, too, that on those rare occasions when a new boy was assigned to his cottage, he always arrived accompanied by one of the shirt-and-tie people.

But even though the Administration Building was four stories tall and surrounded by cottages, no one *lived* there. He saw this for himself when one day Susan took him inside to the breakroom where together they fed nickels into the candy machine. She took the opportunity to show him around. The only people he saw were people who worked there. They were huddled behind desks, walking between offices, and gathered together around a big table in a big room. A few people spoke to Susan. No one spoke to him. He saw no residents huddled in wards, no cottage staff ready to keep him in line, no dormitories, and no big bathrooms. He heard not one blaring radio and heard no one yelling and screaming. It was so quiet that he heard his shoes squeaking on the soft, rubbery stuff on which he found himself walking. "It's called carpet," Susan told him.

For what he had in mind, Eddie determined that he needed at least three hoses. Hoses were plentiful at Orient since seemingly everything at the institution was hosed down at some point during the day. He swiped the first two hoses from the deep sinks in the dayrooms in Wards 4 and 5 since he knew that the lower-functioning guys who lived there would not protest. The third hose he took from the "slop sink" in the bathroom on Ward 3, where he lived. The hoses were heavy, and he was a small boy, so moving them was hard work. With effort, he lugged all three over to the big building and deposited them in one of the window wells along the side of the building.

After he took a moment to catch his breath, he removed the first hose from the window well and connected it to the faucet on the outside of the building. Then he removed the nozzle so that he could attach the second hose. He repeated the process for hose number three and stood back to briefly admire his work. Then he grabbed the end of the hose and turned on the water. He felt the hose stiffen as the water pushed against the nozzle, which was still in the *off* position. Cautiously, he entered the building. The eerie silence he encountered stopped him in his tracks, but he quickly regained his resolve, opened the nozzle, and directed a stream of water down the length of the hallway that, at the moment, was deserted. Because the sound of the gushing water was muffled by the carpeting, the occupants of nearby offices remained unaware of the experience they were about to have. Up and down, Eddie directed the hose so that the carpeting along the length of the hallway absorbed the water in equal measure. When the carpeting was completely soaked, excess water began to trickle into the offices whose occupants remained hidden behind closed doors. But not for long. When screaming people appeared up and down the hallway, Eddie burst out laughing, dropped the hose, and ran back to Cottage A.

Arriving back to Ward 3, where children his age lived, he discovered that everyone was gone except for Peter Piper, a young boy who was without speech and who spent most of the day rocking back and forth, whether sitting or standing. Unfortunately for Peter Piper, he was standing near a mop bucket filled with water. Eddie motioned for Peter Piper to stand in the bucket, which Peter did. When the cottage staff returned a short time later, they were greeted by the site of poor Peter Piper rocking back and forth in a bucket of water with a mop in his hand, looking like a strange scarecrow wavering in the breeze.

CHAPTER ELEVEN

Illuminated only by the pulsating flashes of the strobe light rented for the occasion, the oddball collection of staff and residents that called themselves a band pounded on their instruments while lead guitarist Tony Marino, like so many wannabe musicians before him, did his best to master the four-note riff that identified the song as *Smoke on the Water*.

Out on the dancefloor, a middle-aged woman from Maple Cottage worked to synchronize her movements with those of Otto, the working boy who greeted Susan on her first visit to Orient. Together, they maneuvered majestically through the crowd, both struggling to adapt the foxtrot learned in their youth to the piercing racket that erupted from the electric guitars. Elsewhere on the dancefloor, the muscular teenager they called Boxer pawed the air with clenched fists, gyrating with the beat as he rocked back and forth in his distinctive manner, happy to be part of the throng.

Serving as instructors and chaperons, staff mingled with the crowd, encouraging those who were reluctant to participate but intervening when dancing gave way to more intimate explorations. And when an accidental collision caused tempers to flare, they redirected the potential combatants so skillfully that the intervention went unnoticed. All were participants in the annual dance, a rare celebration in a place of such monotonous sameness that even Christmas Day was unnoticed by most.

Following Tony's exaggerated example, the band strummed on, each musician playing at a tempo dictated mostly by his own ability, each proud to be associated with such glorious pandemonium. All around them, the residents danced on, some moving with a deftness that reflected an innate ability while others just hopped about. All were surprised and pleased that their wild expressiveness was for once not censured, although one man who skipped around the room astride what appeared to be a wooden fence post was firmly instructed to dismount.

Susan watched it all while she kept one eye on the Boxer. "The dance ain't no place for low grades," Annabelle had told her before they left, but Susan disagreed. "If you treat people like they're normal, they'll act normal," she replied. So far, her prediction has been accurate. The Boxer's bizarre routine would have been appropriate at the high school homecoming dance, masked as it was by the strobe light and accompanied by music. With his natural good looks enhanced further by new slacks and sports shirt, which Susan had purchased for the occasion, he might even pass as the King of the Court.

It does us all good to get dressed up once in a while, Susan thought. She liked the way she looked too, although, from the way that even the Boxer had eyed her, she worried vaguely that her skirt was too short and her blouse too tight. But she brushed aside her concern when she spotted Eddie in the back of the room and noticed that he stood with his hands over his ears. She picked her way through the crowd and pulled one hand away from the side of his head. "Too loud?"

Eddie nodded and put his hand back over his ear.

"I heard you got into quite a bit of trouble today."

Eddie smiled but said nothing.

The episode at the Administration Building was causing a large stir, but it was the episode with Peter Piper that troubled Susan the most. "Why did you do that to Peter Piper?"

Eddie said nothing, but the smile vanished.

Susan looked around the room to locate the Boxer. Then she looked back at Eddie. "You know you don't have to stay here if the music hurts your ears."

As she watched Eddie navigate toward the exit, she spotted the M&M Boys, Mitch, and Mark, sitting against the far wall. The children of Mathew and Mary Stewart, the twins, were named so that everyone in the family would have the same initials, the parents' first act in what would have been an orchestrated effort to link their own identity to the hoped-for achievements of the children. But when their disabilities were diagnosed, they were sent to Orient.

Susan coaxed Mitch onto the dance floor and away from his brother, Mark. Left alone, Mark did what he often did when separated from his brother. He banged his forehead slowly and deliberately against the wall, opening lacerations that had only recently healed from a prior episode. By the time Susan returned, the head-banging had stopped, and Mark was sitting peacefully with blood streaming down his nose and into his lap. But when she turned around to call for assistance, she discovered an even more urgent problem. The Boxer was gone.

Quickly, she inspected the room, then stood on a chair for a better view. No Boxer. She left the dance hall and retraced her steps back to the ward. Finding it dark and empty, she hurried downstairs to the dormitory to tell Annabelle.

"I ain't seen him," Annabelle said before Susan could utter a word. "But you best find him."

Outside, Susan paused to let her eyes adjust to the darkness, then dashed through the parking lot to the adjoining playground. Feeling the first stirring of panic, she willed herself to calm down. She removed a cigarette from a freshly opened pack, looked furtively in all directions, then lit it and took a deep drag.

The Boxer hit her like a football player hitting a tackling dummy. Susan screamed once and went down in a heap. While she gasped for breath, the Boxer grabbed at her skirt but got a handful of her blouse. He ripped it off and pulled Susan toward him. When she resisted, the Boxer lay across her so that she couldn't move. He thrust his hand deep into the skirt pocket, jerking free the pack of cigarettes. First, he tore away the packaging with his teeth, then he stuffed as many as he could into his mouth, filters intact. A few seconds of chewing and swallowing made room for the rest. All that was left was Susan's still glowing cigarette, and he swallowed it too. When he was done, he rolled off of Susan and sat up.

Susan pulled herself into a sitting position, gathered her shredded blouse around her, and drew her legs against her chest, wrapping her arms around them. For several moments, she and the Boxer sat in silence. Only when the Boxer belched and grunted contentedly did Susan start to cry, recognizing again that she should have heeded Annabelle's advice.

Inside, Mark sat peacefully beside his brother, singing the song that he always sang at this moment. If the tune was unrecognizable, the words were familiar to all, referencing as they did that famous reindeer who just happened to have a very shiny nose.

Not far away in the dormitory of Cottage A, Eddie Fugate climbed into his bed and uncharacteristically went immediately to sleep. Next door in Doren Hall, Otto sat with the rest of the working boys and watched Kojak, one of his favorite television shows. Moments later, the Boxer ambled peacefully back to the Cottage in search of a drink of water. Later, he would go with Susan to the hospital and have his stomach pumped. He would not protest.

CHAPTER TWELVE

Susan knew that Eddie's penchant for building odd-looking shacks with pilfered materials was not an activity that would be tolerated indefinitely, but with Tony's help, she thought the problem was being managed. That was before Eddie hosed down the Administration Building, an act that elevated his misbehavior to a level that could not be ignored. Now even the Superintendent knew who Eddie Fugate was and what he had done. An investigation was launched, reports were written, and meetings were held. Staff was directed to get control of the situation. When they failed, the outcome was predictable. Eddie Fugate was confined to Cottage A.

———

KATE HANLON, the aide in charge of Ward 3, paid only scant attention to the group of boys in whose midst she sat; her attention focused instead on Eddie, who was at the opposite end of the ward. When she saw him move in her direction, a knot formed in her stomach. "Thanks," she mouthed in mock gratitude to her coworker stationed at the other end of the room. Appreciating the gesture, the coworker smiled and exhaled like a soccer goalie who, having survived the onslaught, momentarily relaxes as the action moves upfield.

Longtime attendants, the two women were sometimes mistaken for sisters. Both favored loose-fitting clothes to hide their obesity, and both wore long-sleeved shirts even when it was hot, a necessity to protect themselves from the advances of another Ward 3 problem child, a newcomer everyone was calling Bean, presumably because he was skinny as a string bean. As Kate discovered one day when Bean dug his long, skinny fingers into her fleshy underarm, the young lad was aroused by flab. It was a bizarre fetish with which his parents had been unable to cope and which contributed to his institutionalization.

But at the moment, Kate was not concerned about Bean. "Don't you dare!" she yelled at Eddie.

Eddie hurled his T-shirt high into the air and then watched as it fluttered down, entwining itself in the large ceiling fan.

"You know what that means," Kate said. "Back to you-know-where."

Kate grabbed a broom and stood on her tiptoes to dislodge the shirt from the groaning fan before the motor overheated. She stepped out of the way as the T-shirt fell back to earth, then watched as the old ceiling fan regained its pace, its blades unexpectedly assisted by a freshening breeze that invaded the space through the big screenless windows. Although the breeze was welcome, it didn't cut the tension that had been almost palpable since Eddie was confined to quarters in a desperate attempt to prevent another incident. As a result, the ward's fragile equilibrium was disrupted.

Kate watched now as Eddie careened about, his engine on

full throttle, with no place to go. Although antics like this were commonplace for Eddie, the belly-hugging laughter into which he always dissolved made it impossible to stay mad at him for very long. But this time, he wasn't laughing. He was just being destructive.

Kate resumed her patrol with a sense of urgency. Not wanting to introduce additional tension, she talked in modulated tones. "You've been so good about not doing that," she said to one young boy who pulled at the few patches of hair that remained on his head. Gently, Kate placed the boy's hands in his lap.

At the other end of the room, her coworker inspected the restraints applied to keep one of the M&M boys from harming himself. "After the nurse gives him his meds, we'll let him out of this," she assured his brother.

Unattended by either woman, the other boys responded in familiar ways. One stared intently at the television mounted high on the wall in a steel cage. "Anacin with acetaminophen!" he shouted in concert with the commercial. "Anacin with acetaminophen!" Another boy performed back flips across the room while yet another tore his canvas shoes into smaller and smaller pieces, then threw them into the window well where they joined others previously disposed of. And at a spot that was precisely twenty-seven inches from the entrance to the bathroom, Bean made sure that the back of his chair touched the small bare spot on the wall where the paint had been rubbed off. Although the chair was similar to several others in the sparsely furnished room, this was his chair. It gave him comfort and anchored his world.

After Bean put the chair where he wanted it, he tied more knots in his shoelaces, tucked in his T-shirt, and pulled his pants up to his armpits. Finally, he sat down carefully. Although it was not a rocking chair, he rocked hard, pressing his head forward so that it almost touched his knees, then propelling himself backward. When after a few repetitions, the chair was dislodged from its sacred position, Bean put it back in its place, re-tucked his shirt, and resumed rocking. Because he was unable to sustain his ritual long enough to dissipate the tension, his frustration grew.

Although Eddie had no understanding of why he was about to do what he was about to do, Susan would later surmise that he was trying to regain his self-respect, a hard-earned commodity not easily preserved in a place like Orient. Without warning or preparation, Eddie, at the age of six, was thrust into the bowels of a ward system that forced upon him its daily depredations. But with the occasional assistance of others and with Susan's unflagging support, his spirit slowly rekindled. The acquisition of his bicycle expanded the boundaries of his world, and the construction of his donk house created a space that was his own, a home not only for his bike but for other odds and ends that constituted the entirety of his personal belongings. Now it had all been taken away, plunging the young boy back into the faceless depths. Eddie would attempt to elevate himself, this time by exercising power and control over someone else.

As Bean adjusted his clothing yet again, Eddie seized the unguarded chair, pushed it across the terrazzo floor to the open window, and threw it out.

Had Kate seen him do it, she would have prepared herself for what she knew would come next since whenever Bean was provoked, she was always the target of his retaliation. But she didn't. She screamed as she felt herself being jerked backward. She couldn't see Bean, but she knew it was he who was affixed to her back, one hand bound up in her hair, the other locked to her flabby underarm. Together, they fell to the floor.

Kate's coworker rushed to the telephone and called for

assistance, then went to the aid of her friend. As Kate and Bean
rolled about on the floor, the coworker looked for her opening.
When it came, she laid her body across both of them. Together,
they waited for help to arrive.

Mesmerized, Eddie watched it all. He heard the cottage
supervisor insert the key into the door to the ward, and he
watched as the nurse with the hypodermic hurried across the
room. But when the nurse administered the injection, he
shifted his gaze to the yard below. He looked to see if the chair
was still in one piece and noticed that it was. Slowly at first
and then more rapidly, Eddie punched the air like a prize-
fighter practicing his jab, each thrust of his right hand accompanied by an angry, menacing grunt, while his left hand
remained frozen in mid-air behind his head, oddly juxtaposed
and not part of the action. After some moments, he stopped. At
last weary after a long day of constant motion, he suddenly felt
alone and very sad. Later, when Kate took him to the timeout
room, he did not resist.

———

Susan learned what had happened as she and Kate walked to
the parking lot after work. For most of the night, she smoked
cigarettes and tromped around the overgrown backyard of the
small house she rented near the Village of Orient. The next day,
she went in early to check on Eddie.

Clinging to the faint hope that she was overreacting, she
cast her eyes about the dayroom, hoping to catch a glimpse of
him. When she couldn't find him, she went to the time-out
room and peered through the small glass portal in the heavy
metal door. Eddie sat on the floor, naked and perspiring, an
indentation visible in the hard leather padding on the wall
behind his head. Although he was biting his hand so hard that

blood collected in his mouth, even more, frightening was the look of terror in his blue eyes.

Susan turned to seek out Kate and was surprised to find that she was standing right behind her.

"We had to do it," Kate said. "At lunch, he dumped his milk on one of the M&M boys."

"But he's harming himself," Susan said.

"I know that."

Both women understood what would come next. The medical staff would be consulted, and drugs would be prescribed. Once Eddie was medicated, he would stay medicated.

"Eddie Fugate must never become a low-grade," Susan said with conviction.

Kate knew what she meant. More so than members of any other group, the low grades existed in the manner dictated by the least functional among them. If one man had to drink his food, so did they all.

Susan turned back to the door and looked inside again. She noticed that Eddie was sitting peacefully with his hands at his side, and she wondered if he sensed her presence. Turning to address her colleague, she spoke with an assurance that surprised them both.

"No more time-outs," she said. "We cannot keep locking him up. It's only making things worse."

Kate knew that what Susan said was true. "Then you better figure out what we're gonna do next," she said.

CHAPTER THIRTEEN

For a time, Susan was immobilized by her grief. It took Annabelle's gentle prodding to get her to refocus her attention on the task at hand. "If'n we aim to be done 'fore dark, I reckon we oughta get started," Annabelle said.

Annabelle squirted soap into a bucket, and Susan filled it with warm water from a hose to which a showerhead had been attached. Without being asked, a man stepped forward, the first in a long line of naked and dirty men that stretched down the hallway.

"Raise your arms, Eugene," Susan said, dipping the mop into the bucket of soapy water.

Eugene knew the routine. He stood with his head down, making various parts of his lean, lanky body accessible at the appropriate time.

Susan started at his neck and worked her way down. "You got poop everywhere, Eugene."

When she ran the mop between his legs, he widened his stance to accommodate her. As she had come to expect, the contact with the mop had excited Eugene, and she waited while he masturbated. "Point it down," she said.

Afterward, Susan finished him up, then stepped back while Annabelle rinsed him off.

Because the dimly lit shower room would accommodate only one man at a time, Annabelle and Susan worked fast to get the men washed and dried in the time allotted before lights out.

"One down, thirty-five to go," Annabelle said. "But who's counting."

Susan ignored the attempt at small talk. Instead, she motioned for the next man to step forward. "Herman, you're a mess," she sighed. "I hope you've learned your lesson."

A few hours earlier, Herman had approached Susan with a big wad of chewing tobacco stuffed into his cheek. "Me got bacci," he had told her proudly, just before he puked all over both of them.

"Now you know why you shouldn't chew tobacco, Herman," Susan said.

"Bacci," Herman repeated, smiling at the recollection.

"And the 'bacci' made you sick," Susan said, applying the mop with such vigor that Herman almost lost his balance.

Annabelle helped Herman steady himself, then wrapped him in a towel. "Sometimes this place is harder on the folks that work here than them that live here," she said, trying again to engage Susan.

"I know that."

Susan appreciated Annabelle's observation, understanding that it was offered by a woman who "didn't bleve in messin' in nobody else's bi-ness." Comforted, she turned her attention to the next man, who looked away and put his hands over his eyes.

"I won't get soap in your eyes today like I did yesterday,"

she said. "How about if I put some water in your hands so you can rub it on your own face?"

The man cupped his hands in front of him.

Soon there would be three down and thirty-two to go. Except for when the water in the soap bucket had to be changed, the line moved steadily. Little else was said.

CHAPTER FOURTEEN

After thinking about it for several days and often conferring with Tony, Susan finally settled on the only solution that presented itself. She would assume responsibility for Eddie's behavior, even if it cost her her job.

"We're going to treat Eddie the way we used to," she said to Kate. "Let him sneak away after lunch. Let him slip out when the door doesn't lock like it's supposed to, which is half the time."

"And when he starts another building project?" Kate asked. "Or hoses down somebody else?."

"He won't. I'll make him understand."

"And if he gets into trouble again?"

"Then I'll be responsible."

Susan took Eddie by the hand, and together they marched out of the room. After a shower and a change of clean clothes, she took him outside and into the warmth of the late afternoon sun. His cheeks flushed with color, and the glint returned to his eyes. His confinement was over, and he knew it. Together they walked through the maintenance barns, circled the firehouse, and visited the playground, then they completed the long loop past the cottages.

Later that evening, Susan returned to her backyard, where she sat quietly listening to the crickets. She turned her face upward when it started to rain, enjoying the clatter of rain on the metal roof behind her. After it stopped, she left her soggy clothes in a heap on the back stoop, then crawled into bed, naked and wet. For the first time in several weeks, she slept peacefully.

But her peace was short-lived. When she awoke, she knew something was bothering her. It didn't take long to figure out what it was. She sought out Kate as soon as she got to work.

"Of course you're right, Kate," Susan said. "Even if we can keep the hoses away from Eddie, we know he'll start building things. That's what he does. We just need to get him interested in building something that won't get him into trouble."

"Like what?"

"I had a brainstorm on the way here."

"What?

"Macrame."

"Macrame?" Kate was stumped.

"You know. *Macrame*. You make plant holders and wall hangings out of string with knots in it."

"You've lost it, girl," she said.

"Think about it. He loves to work with his hands. He likes tying things in knots.

"He likes tying people in knots, you mean?"

"There's plenty of rope and string and buttons and beads and other things around here. If we can get him started, he won't stop."

"At least it *would* keep him inside."

"Exactly. But he can't think it's our idea, or he'll never do it."

Amazingly, it worked. Susan provided a variety of materials and showed him how to tie a couple of knots. Eddie took it from there. Before long, the ward was festooned with wall hangings. Then Tony started bringing in flower pots, and Eddie added plant holders to his repertoire.

"Just don't give him any big compliments," Susan said to Kate one day. "Or he'll quit doing it."

CHAPTER FIFTEEN

By the time Susan and Tony loaded the camping gear, food, and six eager children into her truck and his VW bus, both vehicles were filled to capacity. And that was before they stopped to pick up the tents from the Activity Therapy Building and an air mattress from the sensory stimulation classroom in the basement of Morningside Cottage. Their destination was the Valley Farm, a tract of land purchased to provide more tillable land for the institution but which also contained a wooded area and several abandoned buildings.

Because the farm was located on the other side of the Big Darby, it was necessary to go "out and around," Susan explained to Tony, who had heard of the place but didn't know how to get there. When the two-vehicle caravan crossed the old truss bridge, Susan recalled the rainy day four months earlier when she drove over it on the way to her job interview. Much in her life had changed since then, she thought to herself contentedly.

Earlier that week in Washington, President Gerald Ford

offered amnesty to draft dodgers and called the nation to arms in a new war, this one against double-digit inflation. In St. Louis, baseball fans celebrated Lou Brock's 105th and record-breaking stolen base, while in Boston, angry citizens continued to boycott their schools in the wake of court-ordered busing. But on this, the first weekend after Labor Day, in a clearing between the woods and barn on a deserted farm in southern Ohio, a small group whose rank and file was oblivious to all of this hurried to set up camp before nightfall.

Tony laid the tents out so that they faced each other, leaving enough space in between for a campfire. Then he watched while Stevie and Eddie set the tent pegs for the boys' tent while two of the girls from his class worked on their tent.

Meanwhile, Susan leaned against her truck and blew up the air mattress. Earlier, she told Tony that her participation was contingent on one precondition. She would not sleep on the ground. Now, when she saw Tony looking in her direction, she suspected that he wished she had tackled a higher-priority task.

By the time they got the campsite organized, built a fire, and grilled big juicy hamburgers in a contraption they took turns holding over the fire, it was dark. After Tony got the boys settled in his tent and Susan got the girls settled in hers, they unrolled their sleeping bags in front of each hatch on the theory that if anyone were to try to leave, one of them would be awakened. Then they lay down on top of their sleeping bags and enjoyed the moment.

"So you agree this was a good idea?" Tony asked.

"I'm still withholding judgment," Susan said, her feigned dubiousness belied by the sparkle in her eyes.

"I feel like a reg-lar Dan'l Boone," Tony said, his head propped on one arm.

"Then I'll get you a coon-skin cap for Christmas."

"That would be nice."

"Except that I don't think Daniel Boone hauled a tent and sleeping bags around in the back of a truck," Susan said.

"Maybe not."

"Were you a Boy Scout?"

"Nope."

"I was in 4-H," Susan said. "We raised pigs and cooked and stuff, but we never went camping."

"City kids don't do 4-H."

"What do city kids do?"

"Mainly, we had gang wars and beat each other up."

"Were you a shark or a jet?"

"Mostly, I just hung out with Officer Krupke."

As the campfire died down, the full moon became more prominent. Tony thought that Susan looked beautiful, and he told her so. She thanked him without feeling compelled to return the compliment.

Everyone got up at sunrise. Against the coolness of the morning, they huddled around a freshly rebuilt fire and drank hot chocolate. After a breakfast of scrambled eggs and bacon that took longer than expected to prepare, the group explored the barn.

When Tony pushed aside the creaky barn door, a flock of birds flew out, startling everyone. For a moment, a degree of caution was introduced into the incipient exploration as some in the group wondered if other creatures might spring forth. But this was forgotten when, inside the barn, someone spotted the rusted hulk of an old tractor. Eddie got to it first and scrambled onto its seat, grasping the steering wheel with both hands. But holding onto a prize that others coveted held no fascination for Eddie, and he bounded off to explore the maze of old stalls filled with junk.

As he ran off, Susan watched him out of the corner of her

eye like the mother who is always aware of her child when he is part of a large group. "Horses used to live in those stalls," she called to him.

The boy they called Junior clambered onto the tractor next and refused to get down, so Tony gently dragged him from his perch. As Tony groaned with exaggerated effort and pretended to stagger under Junior's weight, everyone laughed, and Junior squealed with delight. After that, no one stepped down voluntarily.

Finding nothing of interest in the horse stalls, Eddie climbed the ladder to the hayloft, followed soon thereafter by two of the girls. Relieved to make it to the top, all three transferred themselves cautiously from ladder to loft, crawling quickly away from the edge. When Tony saw Junior looking up enviously, he offered assistance, following him as he climbed up. Junior whooped exuberantly when he made it to the top, then inched back cautiously toward the edge to get a better look at Susan. Cackling, he pushed some loose hay over the edge, engulfing Susan, who screamed in mock horror before leaning forward to let the straw fall from her hair.

After a lunch of hot dogs and baked beans warmed up in the cans, the group went on a hike. They collected buckeyes from the base of Ohio's official tree. They learned the difference between mushrooms and toadstools and discovered how to identify poison ivy. They examined animal holes, got tangled in raspberry bushes, and followed a garter snake through the grass until it disappeared.

Later in the afternoon, the group broke camp and returned to the institution. As tired but happy campers spilled from the vehicles, Tony and Susan hugged everyone who wanted to be hugged, then watched as they scurried off to participate in the evening routine. After Susan and Tony returned the tents, they took the air mattresses back to the sensory stimulation class-room in the basement of Morningside Cottage.

Three stories tall in the center with two-story wings on each side, Morningside Cottage and its companion Sunnyside Cottage were two of the larger buildings at Orient. When Tony wanted to transform a visitor into an advocate for change, he took them through Morningside Cottage, the final destination for the medically fragile, non-ambulatory residents, most of whom were bedridden. Before a new hospital was built, residents, upon their death, were delivered to the morgue in the basement, then buried on the ground. But after the new hospital opened, the morgue was taken over by a group of teachers who created what they called a sensory stimulation room. It was a place where residents could be exposed to new sights, sounds, smells, and touches. So completely was the room transformed that the only visible evidence of its previous use was the cement slab which once supported the embalming table but now supported a large tropical fish tank.

As Tony groped his way toward the fish tank, Susan waited in the dark by the door until he flicked on the hood light, providing enough light for her to join him. Susan was immediately transfixed by the aquarium, where the sudden intrusion of light captured its occupants still in nocturnal repose. She watched as the fish began to move about, shaking off their lingering somnolence before moving toward the surface in search of the food that always appeared whenever their world was suddenly illuminated.

But Susan was soon captivated by the larger scene that became visible as Tony introduced more light into the room. She smiled as bubble tubes and Lava Lamps churned to life, their internal waters roiled with colorful, gooey, hypnotic globs. And when Tony activated the ropes of Christmas tree lights strung along the ceiling, she tilted her head upward to

watch ersatz stars sparkle in the indoor heavens. Soon thereafter, she felt a gentle breeze against her face and then the
fragrant smell of lavender. Relaxed and invigorated, she experienced the room's full effects. But her absorption at the
moment was interrupted by the glancing blow of a soft rubber
ball that bounced off of her cheek. Although she knew who had
thrown it, she had lost track of the pitcher's whereabouts.

"Over here," Tony said, speaking from his position in the
corner of the room where he sat partially submerged in an
enclosure filled with soft, spongy rubber balls of various sizes
and shades of blue. "Come visit my ball pool, he said," as he
roiled its surface with eggbeater arms.

"How's the water in there?"

"Come in and see for yourself."

"You'll have to give me a moment while I change into my
ball pool suit," she said.

Susan fingered the top button on a baggy flannel shirt that,
in a curious way, seemed to heighten her femininity. Without
hurrying, she unbuttoned her shirt, pushed it off of her shoulders, and let it slide to the floor. Then she eased out of her blue
jeans and panties in one motion. Naked for the first time in
Tony's presence, she stood naturally and comfortably before
him. The reflected light from above played off of her blonde
hair and accentuated firm breasts that complimented her body
without dominating it.

"I guess your ball pool suit is the same as your birthday
suit," Tony said in a suddenly husky voice.

"Your powers of observation remain underwhelming," she
said, wading in.

She dove into his arms as if he was part of the crashing
surf, and together, they tumbled backward, disappearing into
the frothy blue rubber. Their reappearance found them
immersed in a passionate embrace, both savoring the contrast

created by one naked body pressed against another that is fully clothed. When, after some moments, Tony felt an increasing urgency to shed his own clothes, he did so with far less grace. Hopping around like a kid on a pogo stick, he tried without success to extricate one foot from its position in a snarled pant leg. Finally, he collapsed backward into the ball pool where, from his submerged position, he could hear Susan's sweet, muffled laughter. It made him laugh, too. When at last he freed himself, he flung his pants into the air in mock victory before he disappeared back below the surface where, humiliated, he would remain forever.

"You poor thing," Susan said, crawling toward him. "You must be exhausted."

As Tony looked up at the face that hovered above him, he knew he was looking into the eyes of the woman with whom he wanted to spend the rest of his life. But it was she who first articulated their shared thought.

"I love you, Tony Marino," she said.

She lingered above him for a moment until the silent reverberation of those powerful words subsided. Then she leaned down and kissed him, engulfing his head in her hair. It was a kiss from which he extracted himself only after he had rolled over to assume a position on top of her, perhaps understanding, as she may also have, that the power of peace-loving words is intensified when delivered from a position of dominance. "I love you too," he said.

For some moments, they huddled in the surf. They enjoyed the starry night and felt the gentle breeze against their faces as together they came slowly to see each other against the expanded dimensions of a suddenly deeper relationship. But the gentle caresses were soon influenced by a more primal desire. As Tony had come to embrace new responsibilities, so too would he now enjoy new privileges. With a proprietor's attention to detail heightened by the pleasure of anticipation, he inspected the beauty of this precious new asset, casting his eyes across her full length. Noticing that she still had a tan line even though the summer tan had begun to fade, he could tell that she had been wearing a two-piece bathing suit.

"How'd you get the tan?" he asked as if he had missed an event at which he would have liked to have been present.

"In the sun, stupid."

Languorously, she twisted her body so that he could see even more of the evidence and thereby brought into view what Tony surmised to be a scar on her leg just below the knee.

"How'd that happen?" he asked, gently massaging the small ridge of scar tissue.

"Fell off my bike when I was a little girl."

He kissed this reminder of childhood pain, embracing her imperfection as well as announcing himself as a future protector.

"I think there's another spot here," she said.

After he kissed her there, too, she marked different spots a few inches apart, plotting a circuitous course that took Tony up the length of her body. The rate of progress slowed when he reached her breasts, and she arched her back against the rising crescendo of pleasure that coursed through her body. When she could stand it no longer, she grabbed him by a clump of his curly black hair and pulled him toward her. Neither of them was any longer in the mood for conversation.

———

IN STARK CONTRAST to the blessedness of that moment, the occupants of the basement dormitories engaged in their own nocturnal rituals. Some lay in silence. Others gave voice to prayers learned long ago, whispering fragments both poignant and indecipherable. Some called to the departed. Some called to the never existing. Some cursed their abandoners, while others pleaded only for their return. Others masturbated, some beneath the sheets that provided the only opportunity for privacy, others more overtly, having discovered the freedom that lies beyond shame. Some waited in anticipation and arousal. Others waited in fear, steeling themselves for the moment. And when the only sounds that broke the silence were the sounds of sleep, the "night crawlers" slipped from their beds in search of partners who sometimes were willing and sometimes were not. But as they slithered across the damp mossy surfaces to embrace their prey, there were some in this crowded place that were avoided even by the night crawlers. Among this last sad lot, deemed so repulsive as to be unfit quarry even for such depravity, there existed one man so feral and so disconnected that, alone and abandoned, he fucked a hole in the floor.

CHAPTER SIXTEEN

1980

Eddie surveyed the scene from the seat of his bicycle. Except for the drone of air conditioners, the town of South Vienna, Ohio, was quiet. And Eddie didn't like quiet. Just as quickly as he stopped, he started again, this time riding toward the center of town. As he coasted through the only traffic light, he spotted a new pickup truck parked outside of the Harmony Township Fire Department. The light bar on the roof told him that the owner of the truck was a volunteer fireman, but which fireman? Eddie skidded to a stop behind the truck, climbed onto the dashboard, and looked inside. The familiar ball cap lying on the seat tipped him off.

"Fireman Mike!"

He went around to the back and stooped down to examine the temporary license tag. He read out loud the numbers, memorizing them.

———

Two blocks away, Tony completed his business with the cashier at Shoemaker's Market, then stopped to express his condolences to Ron Shoemaker. "Sorry to hear about your dad," he said.

With the death of Earl Shoemaker, Ron's father, the week before, the small supermarket that his dad started thirty years earlier passed into the hands of the second generation. When Tony and Susan moved into the big house across the street, Ron figured that he would acquire a new customer. And he did. But he also acquired a new headache in the form of a little redheaded kid.

"I haven't seen Eddie today," Ron said kiddingly. "How do I explain my good fortune?"

"I think he's out riding his bike," Tony said.

Ron rubbed the top of little Billy's head. A skinny kid with a protruding jaw, Billy fiddled with the cap on one of the big gallon jugs of chocolate milk.

"Your other two helpers are out in the parking lot waiting for you," Ron said.

If that was a hint, Tony took it. "I guess I better check on them," he said.

Tony stood outside the door and surveyed the lot while Billy jumped on and off of the rubber mat, pleased that he could make the automatic door swing back and forth just like the older guys did. On the other side of the parking lot, two boys wrestled for control of the shopping cart.

"Let go," Stevie said.

Stevie looked like he should have been driving a stagecoach rather than pushing a grocery cart. His big white cowboy hat was pushed back on his head, and his two cap pistols rode easily in their holsters.

"You let go," Jack said, steering the shopping cart with one hand. With the other, he pushed Stevie away.

"If we wreck, it's your fault," Stevie said.

Coming from Stevie, that infuriated Jack. Jack was older, for one thing. Plus, he wasn't the one from Orient. He attended public school all the way to the tenth grade.

"You're the one who's gonna make us wreck," Jack said.

"Will not."

"Will too."

But then Jack had an idea. "Better pull up your pants," he said.

Stevie knew Jack had a point. Even before Jack mentioned it, Stevie felt his pants slipping under the weight of his cap pistols. But if he pulled up his pants, he would have to let go of the cart.

"Pull up your own pants," Stevie retorted weakly.

"My pants aren't falling down," Jack cackled. "I'm wearing a belt."

Stevie didn't like that comment either, but he didn't have time to analyze it. He let go of the cart and pulled up his pants.

When he did, the cart veered wildly, barely missing a parked car.

That was too much for Tony. He whistled to get their attention. "Freeze!" he said.

The boys did as they were told, standing like statues and exchanging epithets under their breath until Tony arrived.

"Everything okay here, sheriff?" Tony asked.

"Yep," Stevie said, not sounding like he meant it.

Before Stevie or Jack could accuse each other of starting the argument, Tony changed the subject. "We need to get home so Mickey Mantle here won't miss his game," he said, referring to Jack, who was wearing his baseball uniform in anticipation of the Little League game that would be played after supper.

As the group waited to cross the street, Eddie pedaled by without looking at them. He turned up the driveway, jumped off of his bike, and ran into the house. He bounded up the stairs to his bedroom, slamming the door behind him.

But although the street was clear, Tony didn't move from the curb. His attention was focused on the big yellow bus stopped at the traffic light. He could tell from a distance that it contained adults, not children. His suspicions were confirmed when it rumbled by. He scanned the faces of its disabled passengers, searching for someone he might recognize, then watched to see if the bus turned into the Sharonview Nursing Home on the edge of town. It did.

Sharonview had started out as the South Vienna Motel, built on the theory that its location on U.S. Route 40 between Dayton and Columbus would assure its success. Its owners prospered for a decade or so, but when the Interstate was completed, the motel went out of business. New owners converted half of it into a traditional nursing home and the other half into an Intermediate Care Facility, as the wing for adults with intellectual disabilities was called.

Tony watched the passengers slowly disembark, depressed by the knowledge that these new residents would likely be just as isolated in the nursing facility as they had been at Orient, from which he was sure they were being transferred. He knew that large institutions like Orient were being closed nation-wide, either torn down or converted to other uses—like a prison, in Orient's case.

———————

WHEN SUSAN HEARD the grocery cart clank up the driveway, she felt the warm flutter in her stomach that she still felt when Tony approached. She heard him enter, but she didn't look up from the sink to acknowledge him.

"Did you see what's happening down the street?" he asked, plopping a sack of groceries on the kitchen table.

She waited for him to tell her, but he didn't. Instead, he moved his gaze down the length of her body. She turned away from the sink to accommodate him as he gently patted her tummy.

"I think you're starting to show," he said.

"Maybe."

Tony kissed her, but Susan cut it short when she remembered Eddie's furtive entrance. "I almost forgot!" she said, pulling away.

"Forgot what?"

"Eddie just disappeared into his room. He's up to something."

But just then, Jack came in with a sack of groceries. "My game starts in an hour," he said, putting his sack down on the table next to Tony's. "And Billy is outside trying to get the top off of the chocolate milk."

Billy came in carrying the evidence, the dejected look of a failed safecracker on his face.

"You don't take food out of the bags until we get home," Jack lectured.

Billy was the only one of the guys that didn't react to Jack's bossiness, being too slow to discern it.

"Put it in the refrigerator, Billy," Susan said, partly to direct Billy and partly to get Jack off the case. She placed a hand on each of Jack's shoulders and turned him around. "You, young man, need to go and get your stuff ready."

Jack was so small that observers often assumed he was the batboy, but he wanted so badly to join the team that Tony persuaded the coach to take him. He played only in the final inning and then only if the outcome was not in doubt. Once Jack even got to bat, drawing a walk on four straight balls like the little person who, many years before, was inserted into the St. Louis Cardinals' lineup to confound the opposing pitcher.

"So, what is happening down the street?" Susan asked, remembering Tony's earlier question.

"We've got some new neighbors down at Sharonview," he said. "A whole busload."

"Where are they coming from?" But she answered her own question before Tony could respond. "From Orient!"

Memories of her previous life flooded back. She thought briefly about how much had changed. Within a period of a few weeks, they got married and bought a home in "downtown" South Vienna. It was a spacious and elegant frame house that had once been owned by Harvey Haddix, the former journeyman pitcher who threw a perfect game for thirteen innings for the Philadelphia Phillies—and lost. But Tony and Susan didn't buy the property from Harvey Haddix. And it was no longer an ordinary home but a group home operated by proprietors who wanted to retire.

Billy and Jack, and five other young men were living in the home when Tony and Susan bought it. They were soon joined by Eddie. A few weeks after Eddie arrived, Tony went to Orient and picked up Tony's little friend Stevie and his former student Tank, the window breaker. With guidance from Tony and Susan, Tank had made so much progress that he was able to move back home, creating their first vacancy in a group home licensed for ten individuals.

"If they're from Orient, maybe we might know some of them," Susan said.

"Maybe. But it's only one busload out of thousands of people."

———

IN AN UPSTAIRS BEDROOM, Eddie examined his completed project. His cardboard replica of Fireman Mike's temporary license tag was exactly the right size. The numbers were the same, too, even if they were crudely drawn, typical of a person whose writing skills would never progress beyond the most rudimentary level. He concealed the finished product beneath his T-shirt, dashed down the stairs, jumped on his bike, and rode back to the firehouse. Squatting behind Mike's new truck, he removed the temporary paper tag from the truck's bumper and taped his crude duplicate in its place. The first of what would arguably become the largest collection of temporary license tags in the United States was now his.

———

DURING THE DAY, Fireman Mike worked on the assembly line at "The International," the big truck plant north of Springfield. Single and with time on his hands, he joined the volunteer fire department, both for the camaraderie and for the action, or at least the potential for action. Now as he left for work, he was more tired than he should have been, having stayed at the fire station too long the night before chewing the fat. For years, they'd been talking about building a new facility on the edge of town, but so far, it was nothing but talk.

Fireman Mike pulled onto Interstate 70 and accelerated, smiling when he felt the new truck respond. Like a little kid, he wished he could turn on the siren and flashing red lights, but his enjoyment was interrupted when he saw in his rearview mirror a Highway Patrolman moving up quickly in the outside lane. He glanced at his speedometer to see if he was speeding. He wasn't. Besides, the red lights on top of his own vehicle suggested that professional courtesy was appropriate. Minor transgressions, at any rate, were to be overlooked. He was surprised when the patrolman swung in behind him and motioned for him to pull over.

Mike rolled down his window as the patrolman got out of his car, but the officer stopped at the rear of the truck to examine the license plate, then motioned for Mike to join him.

"Nice license plate you got there, Bub," he said.

Unable to make sense of what he saw, Mike bent down to get a closer look. But when he looked back up at the officer, he could think of nothing to say.

"Could I ask you a question?" the patrolman asked.

Mike could only nod.

"Did you have some help?" the officer said, his voice dripping with sarcasm. "Or did you make that license plate all by yourself?"

CHAPTER SEVENTEEN

Susan grabbed the oversized baking pan by the handles on either end, lifted it off the counter, and slid it onto the top rack of the new oven. Then she stood back and admired their most recent acquisition, a commercial range delivered only a few hours earlier by a restaurant supply house in Columbus.

After Susan told Tony that she was pregnant, they both experienced doubts about continuing the enterprise. Was this a healthy environment in which to rear a child? Could they focus on their own child as well as the guys? When both questions were answered affirmatively, they bought baby furniture for the nursery and ordered the big commercial range for the kitchen. God knows they needed it. It wasn't possible to keep preparing meals for twelve people in the small range that came with the house. There weren't enough burners, for one thing. And the heating elements couldn't withstand the weight of the oversized pots and pans.

Susan stood quietly, dabbing at a lone grease spot on the new range as she listened for signs of activity elsewhere in the house. Hearing none, she tossed the dishrag into the sink. Then she left the kitchen, first to check on Eddie, who was asleep in the family room, and then to watch for visitors who were already a half-hour late.

Earlier in the morning, Eddie had complained of an upset stomach. Susan suspected that he was faking it so he would be at home when the new range was delivered. At first, she thought she was right since, earlier, he had been a full participant in the action. He had alerted her to the arrival of the delivery truck, then provided unsolicited directions to the driver as he backed up the driveway. But when one of the deliverymen shooed him away, he went back inside and plopped on the couch. That's when she knew he really was sick.

Susan put her hand on his forehand to see if he still had a fever and thought that he did. Then she sat down at her desk to look for the note that would remind her of the name of the visitor, who would soon drop off a child for a trial visit. The child "will be a great addition to your group home," the note had promised. She remembered that the boy's name was David, and she recalled that the social worker sounded desperate during a brief telephone conversation. But then again, they always did. No one was ever "placed out" if things were going well.

She and Tony had talked about the visit at breakfast that morning before Tony left for Columbus to attend a long-scheduled meeting. He reminded her that she would be the recipient of a sales pitch. "Remember," he said. "You never get the whole story."

"So skip your meeting in Columbus, Mr. Tough Guy," Susan replied. "Then you can stay and give them the third degree."

"I would if I was worried," Tony said. "But I'm not. We have our little agreement."

He kissed her quickly, and he left.

Susan knew that she and Tony were good at what they did. She believed that any child would be better off with them than in an institution, or another group home, for that matter. But whenever they turned down a child, she always felt as if they had abandoned him. Hence the rule: never accept or reject a child until after the trial visit was over and he was back where he had come from.

She stopped looking for the note and turned her attention instead to paperwork that never seemed to get done. For the first time, she realized how tired she was. "I'll give myself five minutes," she said to herself, yawning.

She was asleep within three.

When Eddie moaned, Susan awoke. She listened to see if he would make another trip to the bathroom.

He did.

"More water butt," he said, meaning that he still had diarrhea.

"This time, drink the pink," Susan replied, using Eddie's word for Pepto-Bismol.

She doubted that he would. Eddie didn't like to take medicine.

"Did you drink the pink?" she asked when he returned.

"Yeah."

"Yeah" could mean "yes," or it could mean "no," whereas "yeah-yeah" said rapidly, as if it was one word, always meant yes.

"Come here," she said, feeling his forehead again. She looked for telltale signs of the pink liquid at the edges of his mouth but saw none. "If you'd take some, you might feel better."

"No."

That was that, Susan knew. "No" always meant "no."

Susan and Eddie both heard the car pull into the driveway. While Susan answered the door, Eddie changed course. Instead of climbing back onto the sofa, he went upstairs to his room and climbed into bed.

Outside, a frail and vulnerable child stood at the front door between two women. Thick curly hair stuck out of the helmet strapped on his head. And his T-shirt was soaked with saliva that leaked from the left corner of his mouth, which sagged below the right.

When Susan opened the door, the young man took off first his helmet and then his sunglasses. She was captivated by his big blue eyes.

"He hates his helmet," said the taller of the two women.

Because her hair was curly like David's, Susan assumed that she was his mother. The woman confirmed it when she introduced herself. Nancy Schultz, Susan remembered, was the other name mentioned in the note she couldn't find.

"And he doesn't like to wear the sunglasses either," Mrs. Schultz said. "But I insist. Sunlight triggers seizures."

When the other woman looked down with an expression of disagreement, Susan decided she must be the social worker. But instead of waiting for another introduction, she turned her attention to the child standing in front of her.

"This must be David," she said. She leaned down and looked him in the eye.

"Yes," said Mrs. Schultz. "He is my son."

Mrs. Schultz usually filled the silence that followed her introduction of David by describing the failures of previous caregivers. But on this occasion, she said nothing more, put at peace by the warmth that Susan directed toward her son. She had the impression that Susan wanted to hug him, and she knew at once that this was the place where she wanted David to live. Her son was a child that no one wanted to hug.

"Hello, David," Susan said.

"Hello," David said.

He held onto his sunglasses, but he dropped the helmet. It rolled a few feet toward the second woman, who leaned down and picked it up. "I'm the person who talked to you on the phone," she told Susan. "I'm a social worker at Children's Hospital."

Susan was surprised. She assumed the social worker was from the institution in northern Ohio where she now recalled David lived.

"David is our patient," the social worker said. "But he's ready to be discharged."

"Except that he's not going back to the institution," Mrs. Schultz interjected.

"That's why we're here," the social worker said. "David needs a home."

Susan stood away from the door, and David entered the house quickly, sitting down at a card table on which one of the guys had left a partially completed jigsaw puzzle.

"He loves puzzles," his mother said. "And when he stops, you can just pick it up and put it back in the box."

"He doesn't care if he finishes it?" Susan asked.

"Nope. He'll just start over the next time."

Susan could not pick up a puzzle until a few days after it had been completed, but she saw no point in mentioning that.

Since David had settled in the family room, the others sat down there, too.

Mrs. Schultz explained that for the first seven years of David's life, she and her sister took care of him. It hadn't been easy.

"David has a seizure almost every day," she said. "Sometimes, he has more than one. And then sometimes he'll go a few days without having any. In the beginning, the doctors were hopeful that his seizures could be controlled," Mrs. Schultz said, her voice trailing off.

A child having a seizure was an event from which Susan had never learned to detach herself. She still breathed with the child and tensed up with the child. It wore her out too.

"Even though the seizures got worse, I managed," Mrs. Schultz said. "Then I had my third child. Almost from the day I brought the baby home, David changed."

"Did David try to hurt the baby?" Susan asked. Unconsciously, she folded her arm around her own swollen tummy.

"No, just himself. That's part of the reason I agreed to the operation."

"Which is why David was in the hospital?" Susan asked.

"No," Mrs. Schultz replied, but she was unable to continue.

The social worker elaborated. "David had part of his prefrontal lobe removed."

"You mean he had a lobotomy?" Susan asked incredulously.

The social worker gently parted David's thick hair to reveal the scar that ran across the top of his head.

Susan was shocked. She had seen many older people at Orient who had undergone the operation, but she assumed it was no longer being performed.

"It was after the surgery that the corner of his mouth started drooping," Mrs. Schultz continued. "And the drooling got even worse after he drowned."

"After he what?" Susan blurted.

"He was left unattended in a bathtub, and he experienced a drowning episode," Mrs. Schultz said. "That's what they told me. 'Your son experienced a drowning episode.'"

"The squad took him to the hospital," the social worker added. "That's how we got involved."

"He's *not* going back to the institution," Mrs. Shultz reiterated, looking angrily at the social worker.

"We're working with Mrs. Schultz to find the right placement for David," the social worker said.

By that, she meant any placement, Susan knew.

———

THAT NIGHT, after they were in bed, Susan and Tony talked about David.

"I know we agreed we wouldn't make a decision while David's still here," Susan said.

"Then let's talk about it tomorrow," Tony said with sleep in his voice.

"There's no decision to make," Susan said. "He's a sweet child, but he's way too challenging, even for us."

In the morning, David joined the rest of the guys for breakfast, then returned to his jigsaw puzzle while Susan made sure everyone was safely on the school bus that would take them to the Five Points School for Retarded Children in Springfield. When she returned, she noticed that David no longer tried to match the notches to the grooves as he had done so carefully the day before. Instead, he forced whatever piece he picked up into the nearest hole, then hammered it into place with a closed fist, causing the loose pieces to jump like popcorn in a hot frying pan. As he sat with his head held low and his lower lip protruding, the discouragement and anger were plain to see. He knew what was going to happen next.

"This isn't going to be any fun for either one of us," Susan said.

When Mrs. Schultz arrived, she knew as soon as her eyes met Susan's that her search for a home for David would continue. Still, she was surprised when David was nowhere to be seen.

"Where's David?" Mrs. Shultz asked.

"He's right there..."

David was gone.

Susan found him hiding in their bedroom closet, scrunched up in a corner with Tony's bathrobe pulled over him, hidden except for his tennis shoes. She peeled the robe away. "Don't make me go back," he said.

"I don't think I can take care of you, David."

But she felt her resolve evaporating. The muscles in her neck and arms relaxed, and her shoulders sagged in relief. At that moment, Susan knew that David would stay. And she knew too that he should not.

CHAPTER EIGHTEEN

To escape the heat of another hot day, Eddie retreated to the cool sanctuary of the spacious porch that stretched across the front of the house. He listened to country music on his "ray-row" (radio) and rocked vigorously in one of the big rockers that, together with the porch swing, provided comfort to all the guys at one time or another. But when he heard the unmistakable sound of a rider gunning the engine of his motorcycle, he stopped rocking and looked up to see a man in a faded blue denim jacket stopped at the town's only traffic light. Eddie resumed rocking, this time in concert with the motorcycle as its driver alternately braked and throttled his machine into a frenzy of barely restrained power.

When the light changed, the man gunned the engine and turned onto Main Street. He rode past the group home and turned into the parking lot at Shoemaker's Market. He jabbed several times at the kickstand, finally securing its release. Then he dismounted and strode quickly into the store, brushing by several customers who were on their way out.

To Eddie, the scene was fraught with possibilities. Not to

be dismissed was the biker himself, who might be tormented in a number of entertaining ways. But of more immediate interest was the ill-considered manner in which the man had parked his bike.

When Eddie saw the bike move ever so slightly, he leaned forward so that the chair's rockers jabbed the air behind him. Then he saw it again, an almost imperceptible movement caused by the penetration of the kickstand into the hot, viscous blacktop. He turned off his ray-row without looking at it and watched intently as, ever so slowly, the bike's angle to the pavement became more and more acute. Finally, just as the man came out of the market with a six-pack under his arm, the bike crashed to the ground. Instantly, the man exploded in anger. He kicked a still-rotating tire, threw his beer to the ground, then jumped back when cans exploded around him.

Eddie leaped from his chair and leaned over the porch railing. All the elements of great entertainment had come together—an act of nature combined with human meltdown. He burst out laughing.

But when the man looked at Eddie, he hushed.

"Do you think that's funny, kid?"

"Ha, ha," Eddie said nervously. "I laugh."

The man kicked a foaming beer can out of his path and walked toward Eddie.

Eddie was scared, but he held his ground. Backing down was not an option. "Ha, ha, ha," Eddie repeated, clapping his hands in mock applause. But he quit clapping when the man kept coming.

Suddenly, the man stopped. *Get a hold of yourself, asshole,* the man said to himself. *You ain't gonna beat up a kid. Especially a retarded kid.* He turned on his heel and went back to his bike.

CHAPTER NINETEEN

S usan reached up to the shelf above the desk and retrieved a notebook entitled "IHP's," short for Individual Habitation Plans. As required by law, the notebook contained a plan for each child, with each plan consisting of a series of goals. The loose leaf fell open to Billy's section.

Billy will successfully brush his teeth without assistance.

"Sure he will," Susan thought to herself. And someday, the Indians will win the pennant again, as Tony was fond of saying. What a joke. Six years later and she still helped Billy brush his teeth.

She thought back to her time at Orient and remembered when she wrote her first plan. Back then, the mandate for individual planning was recognized as a watershed, the foundation of a new system in which individuals would not just be warehoused but assisted and encouraged to reach their full potential. The enthusiasm that she acquired at Orient she brought with her to the group home. During the early years, she worked tirelessly with the guys to help them achieve the goals she had set out for them, but now it was just part of the job.

When she looked up, she discovered that the guys stood in a circle around her. "You guys want to help me update your plans?" she asked sarcastically.

"Nope," Jack said. He said nothing more, and the group around him stood in silence.

Susan was disconcerted. "Then what do you want?"

"We've decided that it's your turn now," Jack said.

"My turn for what?"

"We want to do a plan on you."

It took her a moment to absorb the thought. "A plan on me?"

"Like you do on us."

"What would you put in it?"

To her surprise, the guys had given the subject considerable thought.

Jack spoke for the group. For once, no one objected.

"Goal number one," Jack said, pausing briefly for dramatic effect. "Every morning, Susan will brush her teeth."

"I always brush my teeth."

"*Before* you get us up."

A chorus of "yeas" confirmed that Jack was speaking, not just for himself.

"You have bad breath in the morning," Stevie explained unnecessarily.

"Thank you for sharing that," Susan said, wounded.

"And shave your legs," Jack said.

There were more expressions of support.

"That is none of your business." Now she was mad. And embarrassed. "Besides, I do shave my legs."

The comment missed the point, and she knew it. She could

feel several days of stubble stand itself on end, hideous evidence to the contrary. Suddenly, she felt like a child.

"Not often enough," Jack said, his voice ringing with confidence.

From that point on, before she woke the guys up in the morning, she brushed her teeth. And while she was less successful in maintaining clean-shaven legs, if the guys noticed, they didn't say so.

CHAPTER TWENTY

Susan was in a good mood, and she knew why. Schultzy, as everyone now called David, had been seizure free for over a week and gaining strength and confidence every day. As she herded the small group down the street toward the auditorium of the South Vienna Elementary School, the lyrics to her favorite children's song danced in her head. It was a song that she'd been teaching the kids in recent weeks. Soon, everyone was clapping and singing. *If you're happy and you know it...*

"You're happy too, aren't you, Stevie?" The twinkle in his big blue eyes confirmed that he was.

"You think it's a wonderful day too, don't you, Stevie?"

The twinkle in his big blue eyes confirmed that he did.

"Stevie's happy because he likes the queens," a young boy named Kevin said.

It was true. Stevie loved to see the crowning of the Queen of the South Vienna Corn Festival.

As they ambled along, Susan exchanged greetings with neighbors, most of whom were also involved in the Corn

Festival in one way or another. Some decorated their yards with straw, pumpkins, and cornstalks. Others helped their children decorate their bicycles in preparation for the parade that would occur two days hence. Beginning at the small park on the east side of town, the participants would march down Main Street, then turn right at the traffic light and go two more blocks to the edge of town. By then, the fifth annual South Vienna Corn Festival would have reached its Saturday midpoint, the Scarecrow Decorating Contest having been concluded, the midway in full swing, and the German Polka Band preparing to take the stage in the main tent. After Herman the Magician performed on Sunday, the celebration would be over for another year.

"Who's gonna be the queen?" Kevin asked.

"For the hundredth time, we don't know yet," Susan said. "That's where we're going. To find out."

At the beginning of the summer, Kevin's mother showed up, accompanied by a man she introduced as her new husband. "The kid's coming with us," the man had said, as if he was reclaiming a prized asset that had been foolishly relinquished. She and Tony both understood that it wasn't the kid he wanted, just his disability check. But two weeks later, Kevin's mother brought him back. "It didn't work out," was all that she said.

Kevin asked again. "Who's gonna be the queen?"

This time Susan didn't answer. Her attention was focused on Stevie. "What's that in the back of your pants?"

Stevie stuck his stomach out in an effort to make the object disappear into the small of his back.

"I hope that's not what I think it is," she said, smiling.

Stevie strode out ahead of the pack.

"Come back here, young man," Susan said with mock sternness.

Stevie stopped. Caught red-handed, he bent forward and pulled up his T-shirt to reveal the battery-powered microphone that was one of his favorite toys.

"I told you," Susan said. "We're going to watch *other people* perform."

She had already made Stevie take off his tap shoes.

Susan extracted the microphone from Stevie's pants and dropped it in her purse, closing it quickly to keep the contents away from Kevin's prying eyes. But she realized this was counterproductive, so she opened the purse and let him look inside. "It's just my stuff," she said. "Nothing mysterious."

Kevin had grown since the beginning of the summer. Although he had added two inches and at least ten pounds, the strangely slanting nose that had always identified him as different was still pronounced like God had stuck it on his face during a game of Mr. Potato Head. In an odd way, it fit with his emerging character, confirming an unresolvedness that would make him an easy target or a mindless follower. For the first time, it occurred to Susan that Tony was right. When Kevin's mother and new husband picked Kevin up, Tony had predicted that "all he's gonna do when he gets back to his old neighborhood is hang out with lowlifes." At the time, she didn't see it. Now she understood.

When Kevin reached for her lipstick, Susan grabbed his hand and pulled it away. Tony had been right about another thing. Kevin's interest in all things feminine was not merely a passing phase.

She snapped her purse shut. "Let's get moving," she said.

When they got to the end of the street, the group was afforded its first view of the schoolyard. Susan stopped abruptly, holding out her arms to stop the others. For a long moment, everyone just watched.

Several battered semis maneuvered into place. Others that

had arrived previously were being unloaded by their drivers, weary men in raggedy clothes who would assemble and operate the assortment of "kiddie rides" on which Stevie, for one, would spend most of his weekly allowance before the end of the first day. Nearby, the concessionaires readied the trailers from which they would hawk their familiar treats: lemon shake-ups, french fries, corn dogs, and elephant ears.

Susan searched the crowd for Jack and spotted him helping the guys from the Harmony Township Fire Department. Every year, the firemen erected a booth from which they sold beans and cornbread. It was the department's biggest fundraiser. Ever since Jack was officially accepted as a Fire Recruit Second Class, his love for the fire department had taken priority even over baseball.

Not far from Jack, Mayor Henrietta Hoctor supervised the erection of the Arts and Crafts tent from her seat on a golf cart. Susan loved Henrietta. From the front door of her house, Henrietta could look out across a vacant lot and into the backyard of the Marino Group Home, a good position from which to be an extra set of eyes. With her own four girls now grown and gone, Henrietta also treasured her relationship with Susan. Her husband liked to tell people that Susan was their fifth daughter. "And in a way, she is," Henrietta would always add.

When Henrietta saw Susan, she drove over. "I didn't see your name on the list for the cornbread contest," she said.

Making cornbread was usually a joint project with Eddie, but being pregnant and caring for Schultzy meant that some things had to go. Entering the cornbread contest was one of them.

"If you drove all the way over here just to tell me that, then you have a higher opinion of my cornbread than I do," Susan said.

"I love your cornbread, but that's not why I came over here.

I came to tell you that Bart Spillers is huntin' for Red," Henrietta said, calling Eddie by the nickname by which everyone in South Vienna knew him. "Just thought you might like to know."

———

ON THE OTHER side of town, Tony and Eddie marked the parade route by attaching corn stalks to the telephone poles. Nearby, Billy stared looked blankly at the empty spool that he held in his hand without thinking that more wire would be needed. Up the street from Tony's crew, another group of volunteers stenciled in the middle of the street the image of a ripened ear of corn protruding from its husk while yet another team worked from ladders, attaching to the light poles a flag with an identical image. Doing just one of those things would have been sufficient, Tony thought but didn't say so.

Perhaps because Tony was busy wrestling with the cornstalks, it was Eddie who first noticed the problem. "Wire gone," he said.

By the time Tony looked around, Eddie had already left to get another spool.

He ran first through the middle of a freshly painted ear of corn and then brushed by the man on the ladder so that he was forced to drop his banner and put the light pole in a bear hug. The cursing that Eddie heard behind him confirmed the successful execution of both maneuvers.

When he got home, he retrieved a coil of baling wire from the basement, then bounded down the front steps two at a time. He stopped abruptly when he heard himself being called.

"Hey, Red!"

It was Bart Spillers.

Eddie watched Bart ooze out of the cab of his battered

pickup truck in the parking lot of Shoemaker's Market. In his youth, Bart was one of the area's best high school football players. Now, when he wasn't cooking up one scheme or another, he worked on what was left of the family farm. At harvest time, he employed local high school boys to help bring in the soybeans and corn, sometimes paying them, sometimes not. Fortunately for Bart, he had a loyal wife with a steady job. Why she stuck with him, no one knew.

"Come over here, kid," Bart said. When Eddie didn't move, Bart sweetened the offer. "I'll buy you some three-color."

"Three-color" was what Eddie called Neapolitan ice cream. He moved closer.

"How'd you like to make a little money?" Bart asked in hushed tones.

"Mimi," Eddie said affirmatively, meaning "money."

"Tomorrow, I'm gonna pick me up a truckload of cantaloupes. You can sell 'em from in front of your house."

"Yeah, yeah."

"There'll be good money in it for ya," Bart said.

Eddie held out his hand.

"No, no," Bart said. "I'll pay you *after* you sell the cantaloupes."

"Buy three-color," Eddie said.

Reluctantly, Bart extracted a few coins from his pocket. "And one more thing," he said before he gave Eddie the money. "This deal is just between you and me."

"Yeah, yeah."

CHAPTER TWENTY-ONE

The sign on the tableful of cantaloupes set the price at fifty cents each.

"Make sure you get two quarters for each one," Bart said, digging a handful of change out of his pocket and pointing to a quarter.

"Yeah, yeah," Eddie said. He knew what a quarter was, even if he didn't know that two of them equaled fifty cents.

Bart walked across the street to the parking lot at Shoemaker's Market and climbed into his truck. As he had hoped, people returning from the Corn Festival couldn't resist the salesmanship of the cute, little disabled kid.

By the time Susan arrived on the front porch, Bart had disappeared altogether. "What's Eddie doing?" she asked Schultzy in disbelief, even though it was obvious.

"Selling cantaloupes," Schultzy said.

Susan watched disgustedly with her hands on her hips, her dirty apron ballooning out over her pregnant belly. "How long has that been going on?"

"He just started."

She was mad at herself for not being more on top of the situation. And she was mad at whoever it was that cooked up this scheme as if she didn't know. "Has Bart Spillers been over here?"

"Yep."

She wiped her forehead with the back of a hand in which she held a wooden spoon coated thickly with the residue of soup beans, the smell of which trailed after her from the kitchen. At that moment, she wished she had taken the year off from helping the guys at the Fire Department, as Tony had suggested. "You're not the only one who can cook soup beans, you know," he had said.

"Lots of nice people," Schultzy said, changing the subject.

Excited by the throngs of people that passed by on their way to and from the festival, Schultzy waved in his unique style with his hand stretched out as far away from his body as he could get it, his palm bent at a right angle to his wrist. The King of the Porch, so dubbed because he was the highest functioning of the guys who liked to hang out there, was in his element.

"You have lots of friends today," Susan said absently, still watching Eddie.

"I'm thirsty," Schultzy said.

"There's lemonade in the frig."

Schultzy flung himself out of the porch swing while it was in mid-glide and landed unsteadily on his feet. Then he headed for the kitchen, moving in a series of disjointed leaps that was his version of skipping.

That made Susan laugh. Whenever Schultzy went without a seizure for a few days, Susan always thought that maybe he was outgrowing them. This was one such moment, however short-lived. The loud hollow thump of Schultzy's head hitting the floor was audible even on the porch.

Susan grabbed a pillow off the sofa and ran toward the kitchen. At first, she thought that maybe he had just tripped and fallen, but when she heard his head thumping against the kitchen floor, she knew he was seizing. She arrived in time to see the goose egg announce itself, appearing with the speed of a balloon being blown up. Moving faster than she should, she doused the fire under one of the bean pots that was boiling over, then lowered herself to the floor to comfort Schultzy. It was a clumsy effort. The arm that she held out to brace herself slid out from under her so that she was forced to turn a shoulder inward to absorb the blow. She ended up on her back but quickly rolled over and worked herself into a sitting position. She put the pillow under Schultzy's head and tried to contain him only enough so that he wouldn't break an arm or a leg. Finally, the seizure ran its course, and Schultzy passed into a deep sleep that she knew would last several hours.

When Susan looked up, she saw that the kitchen was filled with smoke. The bean pot under which the fire had been extinguished rested quietly, but the other five now bubbled over. Because she was beyond the point where she could hurry, she began the process of getting to her feet. First, she assumed a position on her hands and knees, then, with great effort, hoisted herself up. While she massaged the small of her back with one hand, with the other, she turned off the rest of the burners. Then she tried to salvage the beans, using her wooden spoon to peel the sludge from the bottom of the big pots. Reabsorbed in the cooking process, she didn't hear Fireman Mike come up the back steps.

Mike entered unannounced, having made several trips already. "What happened?"

"The bean pots boiled over," Susan said without turning around. "What's it look like?"

"I mean, what happened to him?" Mike said, pointing to Schultzy.

Susan looked around for the first time. "Oh, him!"

"Him."

"You mean, what's an unconscious kid doing in the middle of the floor?"

It was intended to be funny. Instead, it sounded angry.

Mike didn't know what to say, so he didn't say anything.

"He had a seizure," Susan explained.

"Oh."

"Hand me that potholder," she said, pointing to the other side of the room where the potholder had somehow maneuvered itself.

Mike complied absently, his attention still focused on Schultzy. "Quite a knot he has there."

"Yes, it is."

"Should we put some ice on it?"

"You can if you want."

That didn't sound good either, so she elaborated. "I mean, I don't think it's going to get any bigger, but it wouldn't hurt to put ice on it."

"Are you okay?" Mike asked, deciding that Susan looked ill.

"I'm fine," Susan said, amused. "Why do you ask? You think I'm going to have a baby or something?"

"Something like that. Where's Tony?"

"He's with some of the guys at the festival. The smell of beans makes him sick. Plus, he told me that he wouldn't be worrying about me because he knew you'd be around, being a member of the fire department and all."

"I don't do squad runs." And never will, he seemed to be adding. "You want me to carry him into the other room?"

"Leave him where he is. I can keep an eye on him. But I'll tell you what you can do."

"What?"

"Bring me another bag of beans from the back porch."

CHAPTER TWENTY-TWO

Schultzy began to stir while Susan and Tony were cleaning up the kitchen. Susan lowered herself to the floor with Tony's help, then gathered Schultzy's frail body in her arms. For an instant, she had in her mind a vivid image of the day when she sat on the floor at the Orient State Institute, communing with Pauly. As she had with Pauly, she now devoted her full attention to Schultzy.

Meanwhile, Tony returned to the sink to finish cleaning up, taking comfort in the mindless task. But the respite was short-lived.

"Oh, my God!" Susan shrieked. "Not now!"

"What?"

"My water broke!"

Tony bolted from the room, intent on implementing the plan that the two of them had gone over so many times.

"Come back!"

"Now what?" Tony asked.

"False alarm," she said calmly.

"False alarm?"

"My water didn't break."

She lifted Schultzy up and held him away from her. The trickle of warmth she had felt between her legs had come from a different source. As usually happened when Schultzy was about to regain consciousness, his bladder had released.

Unexpectedly, it was Schultzy who spoke next. "The horses kicked me in the head," he said, speaking in a slur from a far-off place, the ebullience of earlier in the day erased by the seizure along with most of what he had learned since the previous episode.

Suddenly agitated but not fully conscious, Schultzy struggled to his feet and staggered forward, the first steps in an unsteady, swerving tour of the first floor. With Tony by his side to catch him if he fell, Schultzy journeyed forth on his "walk down queer street," or so Tony and Susan called this by now predictable part of the cycle. When it was over, Schultzy lay down on the couch and went back to sleep. Tony scooped him up and carried him upstairs to his bedroom, knowing that he would sleep for the rest of the night.

As Susan relaxed on the sofa, she heard Eddie run up the front steps. By the time she shifted her attention to the front door, he was halfway across the living room, a large object clutched in his arms, its strap clenched in his teeth.

Susan was stunned. She could see that it was a woman's purse, but it was huge, and it was shiny, and it was bright blue, probably vinyl. "Where did you get that?" she asked, even though she knew that he must have purchased it from one of the vendors at the festival.

Eddie said nothing, held captive by the powerful force that emanated from the purse.

But before she could question Eddie further, she heard the lumbering steps of a pursuer trudging across the front porch. At least now she knew why Eddie was in such a hurry.

"No!" Eddie yelled toward the door.

Bart Spillers bent his head to the screen, then shielded his eyes so that he could see inside.

"Come on in, Bart," Susan said. "Join the party."

"No!" Eddie said again.

Perhaps as a result of this conflicting advice, Bart took up a position just inside the door. "Red owes me some money," he said.

But before Bart could continue, he was interrupted by the sound of running feet. Appearing from all parts of the house and yard, previously invisible children were drawn irresistibly to the spectacle of a boy carrying a woman's purse. Laughter consumed them.

"Eddie is a girl," someone said.

"Girly, girly," Stevie agreed.

"Why don't you put on a bra," Kevin said, strutting sensuously.

Eddie swung at Kevin with the purse, and the image was confirmed.

"Eddie *is* a girl!"

"Don't hit me with your purse!"

Eddie swung again, this time dispatching the group to the perimeter of the room.

"Eddie has a purse," they chanted. "Eddie has a purse."

Susan raised her hand to get everyone's attention. "Can we listen to what Bart has to say?"

Bart started over. "Red owes me money," he said plaintively. By now, he understood that there was a connection between his money and Eddie's purse.

"Let me guess," Susan said. "He owes you because he sold your cantaloupes and kept the money."

"I'm sorry I didn't talk to you first," Bart said.

Susan ignored the apology, turning her attention instead to Eddie. "Did you spend the money on the purse?"

"Yeah, yeah."

"How much money do you have left?"

"Mimi gone."

"You spent all of the money on that?" Bart asked, pointing.

"No."

"Where did the rest of it go? As if I didn't know," Susan said. "I bet you stopped at every food vendor at the festival."

"*My* baby," Eddie said, sticking out his belly in imitation of Susan's.

"You can still return the purse and get your money back," Bart said in desperation.

"Too late," Eddie said.

It was both a statement of fact and a proclamation of victory.

CHAPTER TWENTY-THREE

Tony turned on the television, switched the channel to *Nightline,* and sat down in his favorite chair. A few moments later, having learned that Jimmy Carter and Ronald Reagan were still running neck and neck and that the 346th day of the Iran Hostage Crisis was pretty much like day 345, he got back up and switched the channel to *The Tonight Show.* For the rest of his life, Tony would remember one special night when Jonathan Winters appeared on *The Tonight Show.* He would remember because it was during his appearance that Susan's water actually did break.

Susan would be more likely to remember the role that little Jack played in the whole affair. Just as the bell rang to mark the end of the school day, Jack had a seizure. Attendants loaded the still-addled young man onto the bus and instructed the driver to ask Susan to help Jack off the bus once he was home, which the driver did. Susan hoisted herself aboard, lifted Jack out of his seat, and carried him inside. Shortly thereafter, she went into labor, a fact that she reluctantly shared with Tony, owing to his frantic response to the false alarm of the previous week.

If Tony overreacted before, this time, he was the picture of calm. First, he placed a call to their part-time housekeeper, who had agreed to stay with the guys when the moment came. Then he loaded the suitcase and his wife into the car and waited for the housekeeper to arrive. When she pulled in, they pulled out, making the short drive to the hospital in Springfield. Early the next morning, Christopher Marino was born.

Each night, Tony drove back to South Vienna to sleep, shower, and check on the guys during the three days that Susan was in the hospital. On day four, they brought the baby home to a jubilant celebration. They were pleased to discover that all the guys were waiting for them in the living room.

Susan circled the room, holding baby Christopher low so that each of the guys could see him. But before she let the guys take turns holding the baby, she explained the rules. "Sit down and stay seated."

The rule was put in place mostly because of Jack, who gave no warning prior to a seizure. Because Jack was the oldest and, together with Stevie, the most excited, Susan approached him first. "This is your Uncle Jack," she said.

Jack glanced at Susan in appreciation, then turned to the baby. "We're gonna play lots of pitch and catch," he said. "And when you're old enough, I'm gonna be your coach."

Next, it was Stevie's turn. He looked deep into the baby's eyes and delivered in his perfectly atonal voice a heartwarming rendition of *You Light Up My Life*, his favorite song.

"That was beautiful," Susan said, wiping a tear from her eye. She noticed that Tony's eyes were moist too.

Eddie, who had remained seated for as long as he could, now stood apart from the group, smiling and content.

"Do you want to hold the baby, Eddie?"

After Eddie sat down, Susan placed the baby in his arms. He received it like precious but fragile cargo. Next, Billy held the baby, but only for the few seconds it took to exhaust his attention span. Then he attempted to take his own turn sitting on Susan's lap.

"Not *you*," Susan said affectionately. "You big lug."

Later, when the baby grew into a toddler, Billy would be the happiest. He loved to get down on the floor with little Christopher and play with the rattles and windup toys.

Because seizures were such a frequent occurrence at the Marino Group Home, Susan worried that Christopher would have seizures too. So at first, the baby slept in the same room with her and Tony. But her fears subsided with the passage of time and Tony's gentle assurances, and Christopher was moved to his nursery down the hall. Thereafter, when even the faintest sound of discontent aroused them from their sleep, they almost ran each other over, trying to get to his bedside.

CHAPTER TWENTY-FOUR

Fireman Mike pulled up behind the school bus stopped in front of the Marino Group Home. He waited for Susan to appear with the stragglers, figuring that Schultzy would be among the last to board the bus, but today Eddie was the last one out of the house.

When Susan looked in Mike's direction, he feigned impatience, contorting his face into a scowl and playing his fingers across the top of the steering wheel.

"There's nothing I can do about it, Mike," Susan mouthed silently, shrugging her shoulders.

Mike rolled down his window, glad for the opportunity to start a conversation. "Looks like South Vienna's got its own little traffic jam."

"Good thing you're not in a hurry."

"What if I was?"

"Then you could park and walk," Susan kidded. "You're only a block away from the firehouse."

"I'd rather sit here and complain," Mike said. "Besides, now I can watch Red give me the finger."

It was another one of Eddie's bad habits that Susan was trying to break, without much luck so far.

"Maybe," Susan said cryptically. "Maybe not."

After the others were on the bus, Susan turned to Eddie. "You behave yourself, young man." She grabbed him by the lapels of his coat and pulled him close. "What were we just talking about in the house?"

Eddie was silent.

"For the last time," Susan said, pausing for effect. "No masturbating at school!"

Eddie trudged up the steps of the bus and took his assigned seat by the back window. Because it was the only window that couldn't be opened, it was the only window from which objects could not be hurled at passing cars.

"Go ahead," Fireman Mike said out loud when he saw Eddie looking at him. "Get it over with."

And so Eddie did. He raised his right hand with the palm inward and gestured emphatically.

But something was different. When Mike looked more closely, he noticed that Eddie's three middle fingers were taped together. Recognizing genius when he saw it, he smiled broadly at Susan, then duplicated the gesture for her benefit, pushing his hand up and down for emphasis.

Susan returned the favor.

CHAPTER TWENTY-FIVE

L arry Little was a fellow resident of the Marino Group Home and also one of Eddie's basketball teammates. Even so, he snuck up behind Eddie and stole the ball. "Another clean steal by Harry Spilman," he exclaimed in his best announcer's voice.

Larry always provided a running commentary as if he were a radio broadcaster. And he always imagined himself to be Harry Spilman, even though the game being played was basketball, and Harry Spilman was a seldom-used first baseman for the Cincinnati Reds.

"Can Harry Spilman score again?" Larry dribbled toward the basket and launched a shot. "Yes, he can!"

The physical education teacher stepped between Larry and Eddie and blew her whistle. "First of all, you're not supposed to steal the ball from your own teammate," she told Larry, exasperated. "And secondly, you just shot at the wrong basket."

"Then it's still our ball," Larry said accurately.

Larry knew all the rules, even though he supposedly had an IQ of 55.

The teacher sensed her growing anger and momentarily disengaged, calming herself by again taking note of the physical attributes of the child who stood before her. The perpetually unkempt hair and the faraway look in his eyes reminded her of the futility of her effort.

"Now it's four to nothing for the other team," she said.

"But we get the ball back," Larry persisted.

"You get the ball back."

Larry looked at Eddie as if he was going to toss the ball to him, but instead, he threw it to another teammate. "Harry Spilman throws a perfect no-look pass," he said.

Because it *was* a perfect no-look pass, the player to whom it was thrown did not expect it, and the ball bounced off of his chest. Larry picked it up and again shot it into his own basket.

"Harry Spilman drains another one!" Larry exclaimed.

"Six to nothing," the teacher said, disgusted. "Now let someone else throw it in."

The intended recipient of the no-look pass immediately volunteered, perhaps believing that throwing the ball in was the least risky of the roles available. In further testimony to his good judgment, he threw the ball not to Eddie or Larry but to another teammate. The teammate ducked, and the ball bounced to Eddie, who caught it and threw it as hard as he could at Larry. The ball hit him squarely in the nose.

Larry absorbed the blow and the subsequent fall with surprising equanimity. But after he passed his hand across his face and discovered that he had a bloody nose, he began rolling and thrashing about like a severed electrical wire.

"Everyone, please sit down right where you are," the teacher shouted to the rest of the class through megaphone hands.

Except for Eddie, everyone did.

Because what the teacher did next ran counter to all of her training and experience, she would ask herself for years afterward why she did it. There were extenuating circumstances, to be sure. She would acknowledge that today she was forced to conduct the class by herself since her aide was absent. And she would admit that, like the rest of the staff, she had grown increasingly frustrated by Eddie's escalating behavior problems. Even so, she would never understand why it was at this moment that she chose to speak to Eddie in a manner that she knew would only antagonize him.

"You're out of the game and off the team!"

Eddie was instantly enraged. "I bite you," he hissed through clenched teeth, his voice an octave lower.

"Don't you dare!"

Then the teacher did something that, even as the words were forming on her lips, she knew was also a mistake. "Go over and sit down on a tumbling mat," she said, pointing to the stack in the corner.

Eddie walked to the corner of the gym, slid a tumbling mat off the top of the stack, and sat down on its smooth, blue-vinyl surface.

"Just sit there!" the teacher commanded.

That's what he did until she turned away. Then he unzipped his fly and pushed his pants and his underwear down to his ankles. He rolled onto his stomach, extended his arms, and dug his fingers into the taut surface. Without concern for the reaction of the others, he slid back and forth on the mat. Although the response that he sought he had never yet experienced, he instinctively labored on, hoping that when it happened, the release would bring him peace.

Meanwhile, the teacher tried to calm Larry, who was no longer thrashing about but was still sobbing uncontrollably.

She tried to pry his hands away from his face to assess the extent of the injury, but when Larry pushed her away, she leaned back on her haunches and took a deep breath. A quick survey of the rest of the class told her that everyone was staying put. She knew that most of them were riveted by Eddie's exhibition, which was happening behind her and which, for the moment, she was ignoring.

Eddie rubbed his lower body furiously against the mat. Clenching a portion between his teeth, he spat out pieces as he ripped them off, then plunged into a virgin section. Quickly, he brought himself to a point of arousal that he had achieved many times before. But although he was eighteen years old, his still undeveloped body was not yet equipped to respond. Even as he worked himself into a frenzy, he knew that his efforts would be unrewarded. He succeeded only in stoking his anger.

Finally, the teacher could stand it no longer. "Quit that and pull your pants up!" she yelled.

To her surprise, Eddie complied.

"And go back to your classroom," she said.

Eddie appeared to obey that command too, but when he tried to take the tumbling mat with him, the teacher objected. "The mat stays here."

This time, Eddie ignored her. He rolled the mat up like a rug and held it tightly against his body. Walking crookedly, he navigated toward the door. His exit was made more difficult because the mat obstructed his view. But instead of returning to his classroom, Eddie walked out the front door and started for home. That it was a ten-mile walk along a busy four-lane highway was of no concern to him.

CHAPTER TWENTY-SIX

I t was one of those times when Susan wondered if she would make it to the end of the day. Was it even possible to take care of ten children and a new baby? The pile of laundry in the basement was growing larger and larger. Meals were thrown together at the last minute, and dust rose in layers on nearly every surface. In the beginning, she and Tony had figured that they could get a lot done during the day when the kids were in school, but it never worked out that way. Someone was always sick or pretending to be, and now it seemed like she was called to Springfield every other day to pick up a sick or misbehaving child. If it wasn't Eddie or Larry, it was Schultzy or one of the others. Of the seven kids in the classroom for children with severe behavior problems, five of them were from the Marino Group Home. This time, Eddie was the problem—again.

She strapped baby Christopher in his car seat, backed out of the driveway, and pointed the van toward Springfield. She accelerated quickly, but slowed to wave at the guys sitting in front of the Sharonview Nursing Home. The rest of the trip was a blur.

"You'd think that one teacher and two aides could handle seven kids, wouldn't you?" she said out loud.

She looked in the rearview mirror to see if her little outburst had disturbed the baby. It had not. Then she took a deep breath. "So today, I just won't go to the beauty shop." Like she did more often than not, she decided that she would just get in line and let Tony chop off a few inches after he got done with the boys.

Today, the report from school was worse than usual: one injured, and one missing. She was assured that Larry was okay, so she didn't worry about him, but she was concerned about Eddie. While it wasn't the first time that he had run away from school, it was the first time that the staff could not retrieve him.

As it turned out, Susan found Eddie even before she started looking for him, never dreaming that he could make it all the way out of town. But there he was, right in front of the Melody Drive-In Theater on busy U.S. Route 40, trudging determinedly toward South Vienna with the tumbling mat held out front of him, unconcerned that he still had six miles to go.

Susan made a quick U-turn, then swung around onto the berm and pulled up behind him. He gave no indication that he was glad to see her.

"You still have a long way to go," she said as she lifted the lid on the back of the van.

Eddie said nothing. He threw the mat into the van and climbed into the back seat.

Susan didn't ask him if he was okay. She could tell that he was.

"The school said you and Larry got into a fight."

"No."

"Was Larry hurt bad?"

"No!" He screamed so loud that he woke the baby.

Although the baby's uneasiness was fleeting, the effect on Susan was more jarring. It was at that moment that she knew that something had to change. Life in the Marino Group Home was stressful enough already without also trying to cope with Eddie's perpetual agitation. A solution that she had previously rejected now seemed like the only thing to do.

The rest of the trip to the school was made in silence. Susan was relieved to find Larry waiting by the front door, attended by an aide. She collected Larry while the aide retrieved the tumbling mat from the back of the van. But before she returned to South Vienna, she detoured to a sporting goods store in downtown Springfield. After a thankfully short conversation with an uncurious sales clerk, Susan placed her order: one tumbling mat. Color: blue.

CHAPTER TWENTY-SEVEN

Eddie rocked back and forth to the beat as *School Day*, the old Chuck Berry song, blared from the record player on the bookcase in his bedroom. His eyes were glassy, and his T-shirt was soaked with sweat. Back and forth he went until he reached the maximum point of agitation. Then he dropped down onto the blue tumbling mat, biting and thrusting in his usual manner. When the music stopped, he got up, rewound the tape, and started again. First, he rocked. And when rocking was not enough, he went back to the mat.

Downstairs, Fire Recruit Second Class Jack Runkle returned from duty, having once again faithfully executed his job of opening the door to let the fire truck out. "Did my *Playboy* come today?" he asked expectantly.

"It's on the dining room table," Susan yelled from the kitchen.

Jack picked up the magazine and examined the wrapping paper.

"Nobody's touched it, Jack," Susan said. "They know how you feel about that."

Satisfied, Jack walked blindly up the steps, his full attention focused on the luscious cover girl.

"We're going to eat before long," Susan reminded him.

The knock on the door Susan recognized as belonging to Henrietta. Susan was surprised to see Billy standing beside her.

"My granddaughter is visiting again," Henrietta said too cheerfully as she held up a pair of Billy's underwear.

"Was he wearing his underwear on his head again?" Susan asked.

"Yep."

"That's because Billy has a crush on her."

"I know," Henrietta said with a chuckle. "Fortunately, I don't think she figured out that the underwear was for her benefit."

Susan ushered Billy inside. "Are those for me too?" she asked Henrietta, nodding toward the shopping bag on her arm.

"It's those old *Reader's Digest*s that you like me to save for you," Henrietta said, handing them over. "Where do you find time to read them all?"

"Actually, they're for one of the other guys."

"You mean someone other than Jack can read too?" Henrietta asked, amazed.

"He can't read, but he likes to look at the pictures."

"You don't find too many pictures in a *Reader's Digest*," Henrietta said.

"But there's an advertisement for a record club."

"He's not one of those people that joins every month just so you can get a few free records, is he?" Henrietta asked, only half-joking.

"No, he's not. It's a long story. Someday maybe I'll explain it to you."

But Susan knew she wouldn't. How would she explain that the young man was aroused by things that were round, like records or pictures of records in this case? The fetish was even more bizarre than Eddie's.

Susan pulled Billy inside and closed the door. When she turned around, the intended recipient of the magazines stood ready to accept his gift.

"Take these up to your room," Susan said.

The boy made a face and put his hands over his ears, meaning that it was too loud upstairs.

"Then go in the family room."

Just then, Tony appeared.

"You better make sure your records are out of reach," she said to Tony.

Tony started his collection of 45 rpm records on his thirteenth birthday when each of his friends gave him a different record from the "Top Twenty" of the day. The collection had expanded over the years and was now a prized possession.

"Has it ever occurred to you that there might be more sexual activity in this house than in your average brothel?" Tony asked.

Susan laughed. "So, did you put your records away?"

"Of course, I put them away," he said, offended. "If you think I'm going to leave Buddy Knox and the Rhythm Orchids just lying around, you're crazy."

Susan burst into song. "All I want is a party doll; all I want is a party doll."

"We don't need no party dolls around here," Tony chuckled. "We got *Playboy*. We got the Beach Boys. We got *Reader's Digest*."

"Very funny."

"And I got you, babe," he said, kissing her on the cheek. "By the way, where's Larry?"

"Not home yet." Suddenly, she had a thought. "If I hurry, I can still feed the baby."

"Before the Great Ogler arrives?"

"Exactly."

Larry preferred to masturbate in the shower, an entirely orthodox practice that was underappreciated. But for inspiration, he followed after Susan anytime he thought that she might be about to change her clothes or breastfeed the baby.

"You feed the baby. I'll cook dinner," Tony volunteered.

"It's a deal."

"We'll have steak. 'Rare done,' as Stevie would say."

It was everyone's favorite meal, including Stevie, who found it harder to chew because his tongue was too big for his mouth.

Susan was doubtful. "I can't say how hungry everyone is going to be. They appear to be otherwise occupied."

"They're just working up an appetite."

For the moment, there was peace. Billy, wearing his underwear in the conventional manner, watched TV with Schultzy and Stevie, both of whom still had puberty to look forward to. In his bedroom, Jack "read" his *Playboy*. In Eddie's bedroom, the beat rocked on. But in the family room, the young man had abandoned *Readers' Digest* when he discovered the real thing–a stack of 45s that Tony had overlooked.

His high-pitched scream was heard first by Tony, who went immediately to investigate. The scene that confronted him stopped him dead in his tracks. The young man who now stood screaming in front of him had stacked at least a half-dozen records on his own private turntable. While the lad had no doubt experienced a few moments of pleasure, the subsequent engorgement had anchored the records firmly in place.

Tony inched closer as if approaching a dangerous animal. He reached down but quickly pulled his hand back, partly because the young man was in no mood to cooperate, partly because he had an aversion to touching an erection other than his own. "Shit," he said. "Oh, shit."

Vaseline? Butter? Baby oil? Maybe one of these would work, but from the size of the problem, he doubted it. But whatever it was that had to be done, he wasn't going to be the one to do it.

"Wait here," he said needlessly.

When Tony burst through the bedroom door, Susan reflexively shielded herself from view, thinking it was Larry in search of another peek. But the look she saw on his face convinced her that a tragedy had befallen one of the guys. "What happened?"

"I need your help," he moaned.

It was with a sense of both relief and amazement that Susan confronted the young man. "How did you get all of those on there?"

"He stuck them on there," Tony said. "How'd you think he got them on there?"

The solution was simple, if draconian. "Get me the scissors," Susan said.

Tony was horrified. "You can't cut his dick off," he said, hunching over with his hands on his crotch.

"I'm not going to cut his dick off, you idiot," she said. Suddenly, she felt like the only adult in the room. "I'm going to cut the records off."

CHAPTER TWENTY-EIGHT

J ack held his injured arm tightly against his chest. With his good hand, he opened the back door and staggered inside. As soon as he saw Susan, he started to cry.

"What happened?" Susan asked.

Jack lowered his arm and showed Susan where Eddie bit him just as Eddie entered in hot pursuit.

"Jack took my mimi!" Eddie screamed, his face flushed with anger. He lunged at Jack, but Tony intercepted him, so he bit Tony too.

"Ouch!" Tony said, jerking his arm back. Ignoring his own less serious injury, Tony restrained Eddie while Susan cleaned and bandaged Jack's arm. But it was Eddie, not Jack, that they took to the hospital in Springfield.

An emotional consultation with the psychiatrist followed. Although Eddie wasn't a participant in the conversation, he paid close attention. Just because he had difficulty making himself understood didn't mean that he had difficulty understanding others. He knew that his behavior was being discussed, and he knew that the doctor wanted to keep him in the hospital. The prospect terrified him. It was time to apologize, and he did so abjectly.

"I sorry," Eddie said over and over again through sheets of tears. "Go home. Go home now!"

Susan had never seen a child cry so profoundly. Even so, she and Tony agreed that he should be admitted. They both knew what would happen next. Eddie would be introduced to a regimen of medication so powerful that several days of observation would be required to watch for adverse reactions.

When Eddie came home three days later, he was a changed person. He didn't attack Jack or anyone else. And his obsession with masturbation disappeared. But he was lethargic and withdrawn, and he gained weight so that his cheeks swelled in a way that made him look bloated and sickly. While Susan and Tony were saddened by Eddie's deterioration, they remained fearful of the alternative.

Then one day, Eddie quit taking his medication. He took the pills into his mouth when Susan gave them to him, and he pretended to swallow them, but he spat them out after Susan left the room. Susan knew this was true because she watched him do it. But she didn't intervene the first time he did it, nor the second. After a few days, she realized that she had acquiesced to Eddie's decision to stop taking his medication. While she dreaded what might lie ahead, she was also relieved. Later she told Tony, who was not surprised.

"I always figured it was just a matter of time," he said.

Slowly, Eddie's appetite and energy returned, along with his interest in the blue tumbling mat. And after an absence of several months, he renewed with a vengeance his relationship with Chuck Berry.

"I wish he could at least play more than one song," Tony said.

"At least he's moved on from *School Day*," Susan replied.

"And it *is* true. Like the song says, he has *No Particular Place to Go.*"

Although Eddie was often so sore that it was difficult to urinate, he was not amenable to coaching. "Just use your hand," Tony told him more than once. "That's what guys do." But Eddie eschewed the advice. He labored on in his own manner, consuming first one tumbling mat and then several others, each replaced at the cost of $32.50. It was an amount that Susan would remember even twenty years later.

But then, one day, Susan heard yelps of joy above the din of Chuck Berry. She went to the foot of the stairs where she was soon joined by the other guys. Together, they waited to see if Eddie would appear. They were not disappointed.

Eddie threw open the bedroom door and bounced down the stairs, bursting with news. "The white came out!" was what he said.

CHAPTER TWENTY-NINE

E ddie Fugate crossed Lafayette Street at the traffic light and walked up the block to the Kroger supermarket. After he had purchased his usual variety of junk food items, he pocketed the change without counting it and left the store. If he had followed his usual route, he would have stopped next at Donato's Pizza to banter with the workers. But because his attention was drawn to the site of a new construction project, he walked on down the block.

He watched intently as the man on a yellow bulldozer crisscrossed the vacant lot, preparing it for the foundation.

When the dozer operator finished, he shut off his machine and climbed down.

"What do?" Eddie yelled.

Not understanding, the man walked a few feet in Eddie's direction, cupping his ear toward him.

"What do?" Eddie said again, waving his hand across the expanse of the lot.

"I'm grading the site," the man explained. "It's going to be a new store."

"Oh yeah?"

"Auto Zone," the man said. Then he turned and went on about his business.

————

A DOZEN MILES east of South Vienna, London, Ohio, had the bad luck of being on the only side of Columbus that was not expanding, thereby not benefitting from any of the growth of the booming capital city. Such growth as did occur was concentrated along the highway that connected the city with Interstate 70, the area in which Eddie Fugate had lived and worked for the past three years.

For a time, he and Jack lived behind the group home in an apartment over the garage. A couple of years later, they moved to separate apartments. Jack moved to a second-floor unit across the street from the Harmony Township Fire Department, and Eddie moved to London. His school days were now behind him, too. Because of his affinity for blue vinyl mats, an "early graduation" was arranged from Five Points School in Springfield. He was enrolled next at WeMIB (We Make It Better) Incorporated, one of several sheltered workshops in the area. At first, he was assigned to a crew that assembled parts for a local manufacturer, but after the third time a wrench "accidentally" slipped from his hand and broke a fluorescent light fixture, he was transferred to the janitorial crew. Here, Eddie enjoyed a modicum of success. Supervised by a tough but fair woman, Eddie learned to operate a floor buffer, lawn mower, and weed whacker. But after the women quit to take another job, Eddie was banished to the wood shop, an outpost for others like himself who were deemed to be too explosive to mingle with the general population. He was suspended from the wood shop on several occasions, once for fighting with a coworker whom he hit over the head with a broom (seventeen stitches for the coworker, eight for Eddie), and once for throwing a chisel at his supervisor. For this, he was suspended indefinitely. But after three months, he was invited back. Fortuitously for Eddie, the workshop had received a grant to help the staff work with clients with "challenging behaviors," and Eddie Fugate came immediately to mind. Thus began the process that eventually led him to London and an apartment of his own.

———

With the action at the construction site suspended for the day, Eddie resumed his normal routine, re-crossing the street to Donato's.

"You're late," someone said.

The rest of the workers stopped what they were doing. "Hi, Eddie," they yelled as one.

Eddie laughed out loud, glad to be among friends. Besides, he was bursting with news. "Big trator!" he said, pointing in the direction of the construction site.

"Big what?"

"Big trator, move the dirt."

"Except it's not a tractor."

"It's a bulldozer."

"Big trator," Eddie said again, using the word he always used to describe any piece of earth-moving equipment.

"We're getting a new Auto Zone," someone else shouted from the back of the store.

"Oh yeah?" Eddie said, acting surprised. "What do?"

"It's a store that sells parts for cars."

"Oh yeah?"

Even though there were several more minutes of good

conversation left on the topic of new construction and selling auto parts, Eddie changed the subject. He pulled a brochure from his back pocket and spread it on the counter.

"Let me guess," someone said. "It's a Dodge truck."

"New Dodge flatbed," Eddie said, meaning a pickup truck.

"We're too busy to talk about trucks. Do you want the usual?"

"Yeah, yeah."

After a worker filled a plastic cup full of lemon soda and set it on the counter, Eddie extracted a handful of change from his pocket so she could take what she needed. Then he picked up his soda and left. Retracing his steps, he returned to Goodyear Chrysler Plymouth, where he had spent the morning cleaning new cars in preparation for sale.

———

His affinity for cars and trucks was one of the many things that the staff at WeMIB were surprised to discover about Eddie after he returned to participate in the new program for individuals with challenging behaviors. When he came back after his suspension, he was not assigned to a job in the workshop but was instead invited to join a group of people seated in a circle in a meeting room. Following an elaborate explanation of the process that was too abstract for Eddie to understand, a facilitator asked him to recall the important events in his life while a scribe stood ready to depict the events graphically on large pieces of butcher paper. But Eddie Fugate refused to discuss his past. He remembered his family, but he rarely talked about them. He spent seven years of his life at the Orient State Institute, but he talked about that not at all. "Over. Done," was all that he would say.

In the wake of Eddie's silence, Susan provided such history

as she knew, a role she played readily at the time but one which she later regretted, both because she believed that perhaps she should have honored Eddie's desire for privacy and because the picture she painted was filled with so many negative events.

When next Eddie was asked about his dreams for the future, he was equally unresponsive. With considerable prompting, it was eventually determined that he wanted a "real job in the real world." Working alongside people with disabilities was not "real work," in Eddie's opinion. (Although no one understood it at the time, his isolation from the real world was the cause of much of his challenging behavior.)

"What are some things you like to do, Eddie?" someone asked.

"Drive a car."

No one believed he would ever drive a car, but maybe he could at least work on them.

Those in the group whose job it was to find jobs for "consumers," as people like Eddie were called, were dispatched to find one for Eddie. They accepted the task reluctantly. "We'll let him work with cars, and he'll fail," one person said as she embarked half-heartedly upon her assignment. "Then maybe he'll start doing what we tell him to do."

If the staff had doubts about Eddie, so too did Eddie have doubts about the staff. Assured by Susan that they were trying to help him, he began to be hopeful, except that when the group reconvened, no one had a job for him. The placement team was exhorted to continue its search, but when the group met again, the result was the same. Still no job. On the third such occasion of a "progress" report, the team members, knowing as they did that there was no progress to report, feared that Eddie might exhibit one of the behaviors for which he was well known. But he didn't. Instead, he sat in his chair and cried. He cried silently, and tears streamed down his face.

Frustrated, Susan took matters into her own hands. "It's not about planning. It's about acting," she told Tony that night, still angry with her fellow group members. The next afternoon, she found two jobs for Eddie. They weren't automotive jobs, but they were real jobs in the real world. Mayor Henrietta Hoctor hired him to clean the South Vienna Village Offices, and the owner of the upholstery shop just up the street from the group home hired him too. He kept the office cleaning job for more than a year, but the job in the upholstery shop he quickly lost when he was discovered making love to a leather chair.

Several months later, Susan found him a job prepping cars at a dealership in Springfield. On the first day, Susan washed the cars, and Eddie watched. On the second day, Eddie appropriated certain tasks for himself, like taking used wash rags and towels to the barrel set out for that purpose. On the third day, Eddie worked independently. But he lost that job too when several weeks later, he got mad at his supervisor and scratched the side of a new car with a key.

———

THE JOB at Goodyear Chrysler Plymouth had now lasted three years. Although Eddie was done working for the day, he made a quick trip through the showroom to see if the new brochures had arrived in the few hours that had passed since he left. "They're here!" a salesman exclaimed when he saw Eddie come in. "But just take one. So we'll have enough for customers."

Brochure in hand and with a smile on his face, Eddie proceeded down the block to the RadioShack. Barely inside the door, he greeted the store manager with the same enthusiasm he had displayed at Donato's. "Hi Loolooloo," he said.

Her name was Louise, but when Eddie said it, it came out "Loolooloo."

"Give me a minute, Eddie," Loolooloo said. "I'm with a customer."

After Loolooloo married the owner of the local bowling alley, she and her husband purchased a RadioShack franchise. Because her husband ran the bowling alley while she ran the RadioShack, Loolooloo was accustomed to spending long evenings apart from her husband and their two teenage girls. Big-boned and athletic, she worked to maximize her feminine qualities, spending too long on her hair every morning and still wearing high heels when her feet would let her.

Eddie poked a straw into the container of lemon soda and sucked up a big gulp. When he did, Loolooloo slid the coaster that she kept in the drawer beneath the cash register just for Eddie into position.

Eddie put his drink on the coaster, then stood by silently while Loolooloo completed the sale. When the customer left, Eddie opened the brochure and spread it out on the counter. "New Dodge flatbed," he said.

"It's a pickup truck," Loolooloo said.

"Yeah, yeah. Flatbed," Eddie said, pointing to the rear cargo area.

"I guess that's a good name for a pickup truck," Loolooloo said.

Eddie pointed next to a spot on the fender.

"That's the gas cap for the fuel tank."

"Gas cap?" Eddie asked, acting surprised even though he knew what it was.

"Yep. That's where you put the gas in."

"Keep tank full," Eddie said.

"Me too," Loolooloo said. "My husband gets mad at me because I fill it up even when I still have a half tank."

"Oh yeah?"

Loolooloo sat back in her chair, relaxed. "You know what I like about you, Eddie? You remind me of myself."

"Huh?" Eddie said. He was lost. He tapped the picture on the brochure.

"You have your ways of doing things, and you can't change. I'm like that too."

"New! New Dodge Hemi," Eddie said, still tapping.

Loolooloo leaned over and took a closer look. "Yep. Sure is," she said. "That must mean the new models are in."

"Yeah," Eddie said. "Buy truck!"

"You don't have the money."

"Yeah, do."

"That probably costs... fifteen thousand dollars," Loolooloo said, picking a number.

"Get new work," Eddie said, meaning that he would get another job.

"You're going to have to get more than one new work," Loolooloo said.

"I do it!"

Loolooloo changed the subject. "I guess you've probably checked out what's happening across the street."

"Big trator," Eddie said. "Move the dirt."

"I saw it," she said. "Maybe when it's done over there, it will move over here behind us."

"Oh yeah?" Eddie's eyes got big, and he leaned forward on the counter.

"They're going to build some new apartments back there," she explained.

"New building?"

"Probably more than one."

"Oh yeah?"

"I think they're going to be nice," she said.

"Big trator move the dirt?"

"They'll have to move a lot of dirt, I would think."

Loolooloo smiled, understanding that this conversation would be repeated daily until the construction project was completed. When the telephone rang, she turned to answer it, and Eddie walked toward the door without saying goodbye.

"Tell them 'hi' across the street for me," Loolooloo said, knowing that Eddie would complete his daily route with stops at the Hallmark store and Videotowne.

"Yeah, yeah," Eddie said, even though he wouldn't.

"And keep your eye on the big tractor," she yelled after him.

"Yeah, do." His eyes danced, and the smile on his face went from ear to ear.

———

WHEN THE STAFF at WeMIB learned that a consultant would teach them how to work with consumers with challenging behaviors, they assumed they would learn new techniques for disciplining unruly consumers. But instead of focusing on Eddie's problems and how to deal with them, the group was exhorted to identify his strengths and his interests. Instead of being shown new techniques for making Eddie conform to the workshop rules, the staff was asked to help Eddie determine what he wanted to do after he left the workshop. So, as it turned out, it wasn't Eddie that needed to be fixed; it was the people around Eddie that needed to be fixed.

For some, this new paradigm would transform their lives as much as it did Eddie's, but for others, it would prove only transitory. Susan was among those for whom the change would be enduring. She had always understood that Eddie wanted to be treated like everyone else. And she had always recognized Eddie's energy and his drive, but now she saw his ambition. Instead of seeing Eddie as a child perpetually in need of charity, she began to see him as a man who was contributing to the community in his own unique way. From now on, she told herself, she would no longer call him Eddie. She would call him Ed.

Eddie embraced the change, too. "I man. Three-oh," he told people, meaning that he was thirty years old. Sensing that when he was at the sheltered workshop, he was treated as if he were a child, he refused to go back, even to visit. Although the bus still stopped in front of the group home to pick up the rest of the guys, it didn't stop at Eddie's apartment.

———

EDDIE WALKED to the traffic light, but he didn't cross the street. Instead, he leaned against the post that held aloft the traffic signal. With his left wrist pressed against his forehead and his fingers pointing outward, he rocked back and forth, his right foot in front of him, his left foot behind him. As the traffic swooshed by, he looked straight ahead, absorbing with multiple senses the changing pitch and frequency of the sound waves as the cars first approached and then sped away. If he was a curiosity, it was of no concern to him. This was his corner, and he was at home.

CHAPTER THIRTY

L oolooloo looked down the length of the store. Empty. Unusual for a Saturday night. She finished stocking the shelf, then stood back to inspect her work and stretched her back at the same time. "Eddie must not be coming," she thought to herself, glancing at her watch. "At least I won't be having the same conversation fifty times."

Then she realized she wasn't being fair to Eddie. Even though his constant repetition sometimes drove her crazy, he was still good company. "*Why was that?*" she wondered. She didn't have to treat him with kid gloves, for one thing. Eddie was not a person whose feelings were easily bruised. And he never demanded more than she could give, which started her thinking about how much stress she had in her life, with a husband and two kids to worry about, not to mention two businesses, including the bowling alley. She was on the verge of feeling sorry for herself when Eddie walked in.

"Hi Loolooloo," he said, laughing.

That's when Loolooloo realized something else about

Eddie that she liked most of all. It was his smile. There was something in his smile that touched her soul.

"Hi Eddie!" Loolooloo exclaimed loudly, delighted to see him. The effusive greeting caught her by surprise, so she lowered her voice. "I was hoping you'd come by to see me tonight."

"Yeah, do," Eddie said.

"Looks like you've been to K-Mart," Loolooloo said, noticing the sack he was carrying.

Eddie dumped the contents on the counter and watched as multiple roles of scotch tape and a new pair of scissors tumbled out.

"What happened to your other scissors?" Loolooloo asked.

"Broke," Eddie said.

"You're gonna need bigger scissors if you keep cutting up cardboard the way you do."

"Yeah, do." As abruptly as he entered, he turned and headed for the door.

"If you're going to Donato's, buy me a pizza," Loolooloo said, calling after him.

It was a joke. Eddie would never pick up the tab for anything, including his own meal, if he was in the company of someone who would do it for him. Besides, she knew why Eddie was going to Donato's. He didn't want a pizza, just the pizza box.

After he left, she pushed his supplies to one side of the counter. Then she flipped absently through a bulletin promoting the attributes of a new product while she tried to identify what it was that was nagging at her. It was her little joke about Eddie buying a pizza. She knew that Eddie couldn't understand the joke, his sense of humor being confined to laughing at incidents of physical mishap. She was relieved when Eddie returned a few minutes later.

"You should've waited so you could've just made one trip," she said. "You know I always buy pizza on Saturday night."

But Eddie didn't respond. Already he was at work on his project. First, he cut a rectangular section out of the bottom of the pizza box. Unfolding a new brochure, he affixed it to the cardboard with a small piece of scotch tape on each corner. Then he tore off long pieces of tape and stretched them from top to bottom until the entire brochure was covered.

"It's kind of like your own laminating job," Loolooloo said.

Eddie didn't know what that meant, and he didn't ask.

Loolooloo put her elbow on the counter and her chin in her hand and watched Eddie work. Without removing her head from its position on her elbow, she screwed herself around so that she could see the brochure. "Tell me again, what's so great about a Dodge pickup truck?"

"New motor," Eddie squealed in a high-pitched voice that he sometimes used when he was excited and with someone he liked. "Dodge Hemi. Big!"

Eddie placed a second brochure beside the first. This one was reversed to reveal the pictures on the back. Then he pulled another long length of scotch tape from its dispenser and stretched it from the top of the pizza box to the bottom. Many more strips followed.

"You missed *COPS* tonight," Loolooloo said languidly, breaking the silence.

COPS was the only television show that Eddie liked. He watched it on the bank of television sets in the front of the store.

"Oh yeah?"

"I know how much you like to see people getting busted."

Eddie laughed, and his eyes danced in acknowledgment. "Hate the law," he said, using his shorthand for all law enforcement officers.

"I know you do."

"I buy truck," Eddie said, pointing to a picture of a truck maneuvering its payload through challenging terrain.

Eddie's affection for new vehicles was longstanding. After the move to the group home in South Vienna, Tony and Susan bought a new van. Eddie was proud of the new acquisition, so much so that he transcribed the sticker price onto a large piece of cardboard and stood at the end of the driveway waiving his sign in front of passing motorists.

"You don't have the money for a truck," Loolooloo said, knowing where the conversation was heading.

"I buy truck. I drive truck."

"You don't have a driver's license," Loolooloo reminded him.

"I drive truck. No wear seat belt."

"If you have a wreck, you'll get hurt."

"I drive truck. No wear seat belt. Drink beer."

"That's against the law."

"I drive truck. No wear seat belt. Drink beer. Throw can out the lillow," Eddie said, meaning "window."

"The law will bust you just like they do on *COPS*."

"Fuck the law."

"You know that if you use that language in the store, you'll have to leave," Loolooloo said calmly, hoping that Eddie wouldn't test her by using the word again.

He didn't. He kept working, laying down strips of tape until the entire surface was covered.

"I've got another project for you if you're done with that one," Loolooloo said.

"Oh yeah?"

Loolooloo pointed to a large box on the floor. "It's a new display case."

"Oh yeah?"

"Do you want to put it together?"

"Yeah, do."

Eddie loved putting things together, Loolooloo knew. Susan once told her that if you "give him and hammer and a screwdriver, he'll really get into it," and she was right.

While Eddie worked, Loolooloo ordered the pizza, then returned to her new product manual. She looked up when she heard the buzzer signal the arrival of a new customer. A large, angry-looking man stood at the door. She felt herself stiffen as he approached.

"May I help you?"

The man dropped an object heavily onto the counter. "This is a piece of shit," he said. "I want my money back."

In the back of the store, Eddie stopped working and looked toward the register.

"You didn't buy that here, sir," Loolooloo said.

"Damned if I didn't."

"We don't carry that brand."

"You did when I bought it."

It was at that moment that Eddie appeared by the man's side. "Bad man! Go home!"

"Let me handle this, Eddie," Loolooloo said.

"Like the lady said, mind your own business," the man said, observing that Eddie was a person with a disability. When Eddie didn't reply, the man returned his attention to Loolooloo. "I think I paid a hundred dollars for this thing," he said, nodding toward the object and noticing with satisfaction that Loolooloo was trembling.

That was the last thing the man said. Eddie punched him in the middle of the back so hard that he lurched forward onto the counter, gasping for air. The man lay still for a few seconds, first to catch his breath and second to sneak a peek at his assailant. Then he whirled around with his fist raised. But he abruptly pulled his punch.

Eddie Fugate stood fearlessly before him with his hands at his side. He said nothing. He did nothing. But there was a fire in his eyes, and his face was as red as his hair.

Slowly, deliberately, the man backed away as if from a cobra poised to strike. Then he turned and started for the door, ignoring the item on the counter.

Eddie retrieved a screwdriver from his back pocket.

"Don't do it, Eddie!" Loolooloo implored.

But Eddie ignored her. He threw the screwdriver with the skill and confidence of the knife thrower who hurls his daggers at a woman spread-eagled against a wall. Just like the time at WeMIB when he "accidentally" hurled a wrench into the fluorescent light fixture, and just like the time he whistled a chisel past his supervisor's ear, the possibility of throwing an object anywhere except where he wanted it to go never entered his mind. The screwdriver whistled within inches of the man's ear and bounced off the wall in the front of the store.

"No come back," Eddie said.

"Thank you, Eddie," Loolooloo said, collapsing into her chair.

"Loolooloo okay?"

"I'm fine," Loolooloo said, appreciating that it was the first time Eddie had ever asked her how she was.

"Yeah, good," Eddie said with the smallest trace of a smile, glad to have helped a friend.

CHAPTER THIRTY-ONE

Eddie closed the blinds on every window in the apartment, locked the front door, and started walking to work, detouring to check on the progress of the new Auto Zone. He noticed immediately that the problem he had spotted several days earlier was still not fixed. He crossed the boundary of the site and walked toward the man who looked like he was in charge of the crew.

"This is a hard hat area," the man said. "You need to leave."

Eddie ignored the comment. "Crooked," he said, drawing a downward slanting line in the air.

"It wasn't crooked yesterday, and it ain't crooked today."

"Bad wall," Eddie said.

"Mind your own business."

"No good wall," Eddie said again over his shoulder as he resumed his walk.

When he got to work, he clocked in and went to the break room. Clyde Goodyear, the owner, was refilling his coffee cup.

"Is the wall still crooked?" Clyde asked, hoping that his

peremptory question would make unnecessary an entire conversation.

"Yeah," Eddie said, deflated.

It was said that Clyde Goodyear was a man who "knew what you needed." It was a quality that, earlier in his career, was critical to his success as a salesman and now made him an able manager. Clyde brushed the crumbs off the seat of a chair and sat down. Then he smoothed his tie down across the front of his white shirt.

"Did you go up there today and look at the wall?" Clyde asked, knowing the answer.

"Yeah, yeah," Eddie said, brightening.

Clyde drew his own slanted line in the air.

"No good wall," Eddie said. "Crooked."

"Have they thrown you off the site yet?"

"No," Eddie said defensively.

After an extensive review of the crooked wall, Clyde and Eddie covered the usual subjects in the usual manner. When, finally, Clyde commented that Eddie didn't have enough money for a new Dodge Ram truck, Eddie disagreed.

"Buy new truck," he said. "No seat belts."

"All vehicles come with seat belts," Clyde said. "Seat belts hold you in the seat so you won't hit your head on the dashboard."

"Put pillows in the lillow," Eddie said.

Clyde was stumped. "Pillows in the lillow," he said to himself. Finally, he got it. "You're gonna put pillows in the window?"

"Yeah!" Eddie said. "Blue leller pillows."

Clyde laughed. "You're going to buy a new truck, take out the seat belts and put blue leather pillows in the window."

"Yeah," Eddie said, squealing with delight.

"On second thought, why don't you just buy yourself an

old Ford," Clyde suggested, knowing Eddie's dislike for the competition. "I don't want to see a new Dodge truck with leather pillows on the dashboard."

"Hate da Ford."

Eddie and Clyde both laughed now.

But then Clyde put his elbows on the table and leaned toward Eddie. He remembered he had one more subject to discuss.

"Where were you last Thursday and Friday?"

"Oomp, forgot," Eddie said, slapping himself on the forehead and casting his eyes downward as if overcome with remorse.

"They told me you didn't show up to work, but you remembered to come in and get your paycheck."

Eddie changed tactics. "No work," he said. "Ball big."

He was referring to the symptomatic condition, which, a few years earlier, was corrected through hernia surgery. Eddie claimed a recurrence anytime he needed an excuse to avoid physical labor.

"Susan told me you got that fixed a long time ago," Clyde said.

Eddie said nothing, partly because he didn't know what to say and partly because Clyde had changed roles from friend to boss.

"Money doesn't grow on trees," Clyde said.

Eddie had no idea what that meant, but it didn't matter. He seized the initiative. "I da boss."

"Not the last time I checked, you weren't."

"I da boss. No work."

"No work. No money," Clyde said. "It's as simple as that."

"I go home," Eddie said, raising his voice. "No work no more."

Clyde saw that Eddie was backing himself into a corner. He tried a new tack.

"If you're gonna buy a new truck, you gotta work in order to have the money to pay for it."

Eddie said nothing.

Clyde took that to be progress. "So from now on, come to work when you're supposed to. And if you're sick, call me and tell me."

"I go home—NOW!"

Clyde remained calm. "If you go home now, don't come back because you won't have a job."

More silence. This time Clyde didn't try to fill the void.

"I gonna do it," Eddie said.

But Clyde saw the gleam in Eddie's eye and knew that the danger had passed. "That would be too bad," he said. "Because that would mean I'd lose a good worker."

"I do it, Clyde!"

Clyde unfolded his lanky frame from the stiff-backed break room chair. "I think you better start detailing some cars."

As Clyde approached the door, he sensed activity behind his back. He turned around in time to observe Eddie returning his hand to his pocket.

"Did you just give me the finger?"

"No."

Clyde turned again to leave.

"Clyde pay my electric bill."

Clyde laughed. He knew that Eddie hated to pay his electric bill. Paying for electricity was like paying for air as far as Eddie was concerned. Clyde pointed to the door which led to the service department and the wash bay. "That-a-way."

Eddie turned and left, content with the illusion of having prevailed. For the rest of the day, he would work harder than anyone else in the shop.

CHAPTER THIRTY-TWO

"Have you seen *Lethal Weapon III* yet?" the customer asked.

"It was just like number two," Melissa said. "Only different, if you know what I mean."

Melissa Hart was the manager of Videotowne. A newlywed, Melissa was a natural-born hard worker who was looking forward to starting a family.

"That's what I heard," the customer said. "But I still want to see it."

"At least you will have completed the series."

"Until *Lethal Weapon IV*."

"I heard there's not supposed to be one," Melissa said.

The customer turned to leave. "By the way," he said, "That retarded guy is flipping off people in your parking lot."

Melissa followed the customer out. "Come on in here, Eddie."

It was at this point that Melissa usually explained what would happen if such behavior continued. But not today.

"What did you do to your *hair*?" she asked, her jaw agape.

"No red hair no more," Eddie said.

"What is that stuff?" She pushed an index finger into the gooey mass on top of his head, then answered her own question. "It's hair dye!"

"Red hair gone," Eddie said.

"Where did you get that?"

"In lockbox," Eddie said, using his word for "mailbox."

"You were supposed to wash it out, Eddie," she said.

"Oomp."

"Come with me."

Melissa told a co-worker to watch the cash register, then she led Eddie into the restroom.

"That's too weird," the coworker said to Eddie when he returned.

"Hate da red hair."

"It won't be brown forever," Melissa said.

"Oh yeah?"

"It'll grow back out."

"Oh yeah?"

"Yeah."

When a customer approached the cash register, Eddie stood aside, content to rock slowly back and forth while business was transacted. After the customer departed, Eddie handed Melissa a paper-backed booklet.

She read out loud the title. "Digest of Ohio Motor Vehicle Laws."

The local office of the Bureau of Motor Vehicles was located just down the street in a new building that marked the end point of London's recent development.

"Get driver's license," Eddie said.

"You gotta take a test, Eddie."

"Yeah, do."

"It's a written test."

Melissa knew that Eddie's reading ability was limited to a few words and phrases.

"I do it!"

Later Melissa called Susan.

"You don't even have to tell me," Susan said. "He wants to take the driver's test."

The next morning, Susan went over to Eddie's apartment. She was barely in the door when he showed her his book from the BMV.

"That's what I want to talk to you about," she said.

She sat on the coach while Eddie stood in the middle of the floor and rocked. He was braced for the bad news.

"I know you want to learn to drive," Susan said.

"Take test now!"

Eddie thrust out his jaw and looked off into the distance, but he was listening, Susan knew.

"Every one of us has certain things that we'd like to do but that we can't do," she said. "I'd like to fly an airplane, but I know I could never do that. And it would be fun to ski, but I know I'm too clumsy."

Eddie just rocked.

"And you'd like to drive a car."

"Drive now!"

"But I don't think that's something that you can do."

"No!" Eddie yelled. "Drive car now!"

"Honey, I don't think you can pass the test."

"Yeah, do!"

Susan thought he was going to cry. "If you want to take the test, that's your choice. But I don't have to help you. And that's my choice."

Eddie opened the book and showed her a picture. "Top tine."

"You're right. That's a stop sign. But it's a written test, and you have to read sentences."

Eddie went back to rocking.

"I'm not going to help you learn to drive, but if you want to learn how to read better, I *will* help you do that," Susan said, searching for a compromise. "Do you want to work on your reading?"

"Yeah, yeah."

"I'll find you a tutor."

"Tutor?"

"I'll find someone who will work with you one-on-one."

"Yeah, yeah."

CHAPTER THIRTY-THREE

It was Saturday morning, and Eddie had the day off. As he often did when he was excited, he got up at 4:00 a.m. He showered, shaved, and put on the new suit and clip-on tie that Susan had bought him for special occasions. But it was not yet 5:00 a.m., so he lay back down on his homemade wooden bed which he had covered with vinyl pillows. Because the bed was no wider than his shoulders, he lay on his back with his legs uncrossed and his hands folded across his chest, a position that recalled a corpse lying in its casket.

When the sun came up and his apartment was fully illuminated, he got up and left. For a while, he stood on his corner by the traffic light and rocked back and forth, experiencing the steady increase in traffic flow as more and more residents went about their Saturday errands. Then he walked past the Videotowne, past the RadioShack, past Donato's Pizza, and past the dealership where he worked. He stopped at the last building on the way out of town, the Bureau of Motor Vehicles.

He walked immediately to the counter, ignoring the long line of customers.

"Get in line," the clerk said.

Ordinarily, in situations like this, Eddie pretended that he couldn't understand what he was being told. But he understood that in this instance, playing dumb would be counterproductive, so he took up a position at the end of the line. He rocked impatiently in his usual manner as the line slowly advanced.

Finally, it was his turn. "Next!" the clerk said.

"Driver's license," Eddie said.

"Do you want to renew it or take the written test?"

"Test."

"I need to see your birth certificate."

Eddie didn't know what a birth certificate was.

"Take test now."

The clerk spoke slowly and loudly in the manner in which people with disabilities are often addressed. "First, I need to see your birth certificate."

Eddie took a pen from his inside suit pocket and made a writing motion.

"You can't take the test until you show me a copy of your birth certificate."

"Oh yeah," he exclaimed, rocking faster.

"You can't," said the woman with finality.

Neither Eddie nor the woman knew what to do next.

Finally, the woman broke the silence. "You need to leave."

"No."

"Then I'll call the police."

"Fuck the law."

Eddie's eyes got big as he watched the woman place the call.

When he saw the police car pull up, he left, choosing a path that maximized the distance between himself and the cruiser.

"Hey, Red!"

Eddie recognized the voice and stopped where he was without turning to look at the cruiser.

Before Officer Brad Allen joined the force in London, he was the sole member of the South Vienna Police Department. From time to time he was called to the group home, usually in response to a complaint about the little redheaded kid.

"Come over here a minute," Officer Brad said.

Reluctantly, Eddie took up a position by the side of the cruiser, rocking and looking into the distance.

"What did you do to your hair?" Officer Brad asked, stroking the fuzz above his lower lip, the product of a so far failed attempt to grow a mustache to hide his boyish appearance.

"Hate da red hair," Eddie said.

Then Officer Brad asked a question that was more in the line of duty. "What were you doing in there?"

"Take test."

"What test was that?"

"Driver test," Eddie said. "Buy truck. Drive truck."

"You took the test for your *driver's license?*" Officer Brad asked incredulously.

"Yeah, do," Eddie said. He stopped rocking and looked sadly at the ground.

Officer Brad briefly turned his attention to the chatter on the police radio, then looked back at Eddie. "I knew you were in town because I've seen you standing on the corner by the RadioShack."

"Yeah, do," Eddie said.

"You want a ride home?"

"Yeah, do."

———

ON THE FOLLOWING SATURDAY, Eddie returned with a copy of his birth certificate that Susan reluctantly provided to him.

He took the written test.

He failed.

Eddie came back Saturday after Saturday and took the test again and again, randomly selecting a box below each question, then handing the answer sheet to the woman behind the counter. Usually, he would leave without waiting to hear the results.

"You didn't pass," the woman would sometimes call out to him as he left. "I'm sorry."

CHAPTER THIRTY-FOUR

One Saturday, Eddie skipped the test, going instead to Goodyear Chrysler Plymouth. Clyde Goodyear had been promoting a big sale all week, and Eddie didn't want to miss it, and not because he hoped to buy a new truck. This time the magnet was free food, Eddie being a familiar face at ice cream socials, store openings, or special sales like the one underway today at Goodyear's. But even more important than the food was the big news that Eddie wanted to share.

On most Saturdays, when the weather cooperated, Clyde was at the golf course, but because of the sale, Eddie knew that Clyde would be at the dealership.

When Clyde saw Eddie coming, he held up a hand, signaling him to wait until he finished his conversation with a customer.

Eddie stopped abruptly and started rocking.

When Clyde was done, he turned his attention to Eddie. He already knew what Eddie was going to tell him.

"Wall gone!" Eddie shouted.

"What wall was that?" Clyde asked, feigning ignorance.

"Auto Zone," Eddie said, pointing up the street.

"Gone?" Clyde asked as if he were still trying to comprehend the thought. "You mean it's been torn down?"

"Yeah!" Eddie said, almost screaming in the high-pitched voice he always used when he was excited and among friends.

"It can't be!"

"Gone!"

"I know," Clyde said, laughing. "I saw it myself on the way to work."

Clyde recalled Eddie's unerring ability to spot dents, scratches, or other imperfections on new cars delivered to the dealership, and he wondered why he hadn't believed Eddie in the first place.

"Bad wall gone," Eddie said.

Clyde sensed that Eddie wanted an explanation. "I'm guessing that the wall didn't pass inspection," he said.

"Oh yeah?"

"Any new building has to be inspected by a building inspector," Clyde said. "To make sure it's built safely."

"Oh yeah?"

"According to the building code."

"Oh yeah?"

"Yep."

"Build new wall now?"

"Yep. That's what they'll do."

"Bad wall gone," Eddie said.

"No more crooked wall," Clyde agreed.

Clyde knew that before the morning was over, everyone at the dealership would hear about the fate of the crooked wall.

CHAPTER THIRTY-FIVE

Christopher Marino sat at the dining room table with a scowl on his face. "Everyone else is outside playing except me," he said to his mother. "And I'm stuck in here."

Now twelve years old, Christopher had his father's black hair and dark complexion, but a recent growth spurt convinced his mother that he would have her height. Like his dad, he was good at sports, especially baseball and soccer. Although he was younger than all the guys at the group home, most of them looked up to him like a big brother.

"You're stuck in here with me because you're the only one with homework," Susan replied. "And you wanted me to help you with it."

They both looked up when Jack came in and sat down at the table, too.

"There you go, Christopher," Susan said. "Now you're not the only one who's inside."

"Except that Jack's here because he wants to be here."

Jack took a piece of paper and started writing.

"I've got to be honest," Susan said to Christopher. "I was never good at algebra."

"Please Excuse My Dear Aunt Sally," Jack said.

"I can only help one person at a time, Jack," Susan said too sharply.

"I can never remember what you're supposed to do first," Christopher said.

"Please Excuse My Dear Aunt Sally," Jack said again.

Now Susan was exasperated. "We're working on something very hard here, Jack. You can't compete for my attention every time I sit down with Christopher."

"But..."

"If you're going to write a letter to your Aunt Sally, you'll just have to do it by yourself."

Jack sat back and watched, disgusted.

"Maybe you add before you multiply," Susan speculated.

"I tried that already," Christopher said.

That was too much for Jack. "First, you multiply or divide," he said. "Then you add or subtract. That's what 'My Dear Aunt Sally' means. Multiply or Divide. Add or Subtract."

Susan and Christopher understood their mistake too late.

"If you need any more help, don't bother to call me," Jack said haughtily as he left.

"I guess we had that coming," Susan said.

CHAPTER THIRTY-SIX

For three days in a row, Schultzy was sent home from school early. On the fourth day, Susan sensed trouble as soon as he walked through the door. First, he threw his book bag into a corner, then he pulled out a book and ripped out pages by the handful.

"Wouldn't you rather watch TV than rip up a school book?" Susan asked, making a concerted effort to remain calm.

"I hate you," Schultzy said in a deep voice that sounded like it belonged to someone else.

"You're missing *The Price is Right*," Susan said. "You should go in the other room and watch it with Billy."

"I hate this house," he growled. "I hate everybody in it."

Schultzy went through a bad period when baby Christopher came home from the hospital, but it was nothing like this. Recently, he had started breaking things. At first, it was just dishes, but during the past month, he had smashed three windows.

"We don't talk like that," Susan said evenly. "You need to go upstairs to your room."

Schultzy picked up another book and threw it at Susan, then screamed profanities all the way up the stairs.

Susan returned to the kitchen to listen for more signs of trouble. She didn't have to wait long. She knew from the sound of the crash that Schultzy had tipped over his fish tank.

"I hope you die," Schultzy said when she came to investigate.

She filled a glass with water and retrieved several flopping fish.

"I'm gonna burn this motherfuckin' house!" Schultzy screamed.

The larger shards of glass she picked up, the smaller ones she swept into a pile.

Schultzy grabbed a lamp from the bedstand, ripped the cord out of the socket, and threw it across the room. "I'm gonna burn all you motherfuckers."

––––––––

SUSAN KNEW that a decision had to be made, and not just regarding what to do about Schultzy. She was beginning to think that Tony had been right. A month after Jack and Eddie moved to their apartments, Tony suggested that maybe it was time to do something other than run a group home. "I don't think I'm ready yet," Susan had said, but she did agree that the two vacancies they had at the moment would not be filled. To make up for the lost income, Tony took a part-time job as a probation officer.

Thank God Tony will be home soon, Susan thought.

At work, Tony found himself watching the clock. He was anxious to get home, suspecting that his wife needed his support. The glass of wine that he saw on the counter when he arrived told him he was right. For Susan, a few sips of wine while she prepared the evening meal was therapeutic, the intake of alcohol being less important than the conscious effort to relax that went along with it.

Tony wrapped one arm around his wife's waist. When she made available only her cheek, he kissed it. But before he asked about her struggles with Schultzy, he asked about their son. "Where's Christopher?"

"Down at Jack's, playing *Nintendo*," Susan said.

When Susan was upset, Tony was drawn closer to her. Feeling a surge of affection, he warmed to the challenge of improving her mood.

"That's very interesting," he said with feigned gravity. He picked up a banana and put it in his mouth as if it were a pipe. Then, with his hands coupled behind his back, he paced the floor in studied concentration. "So Christopher is down at Jack's. And he's playing *Nintendo*," he said in a voice muffled by the banana.

"Yep," Susan said, not taking the bait.

Tony removed the banana and shifted his gaze to his wife. "For you, it's as simple as that. But I see a piece of good news."

"And what might that be?"

"At least at the moment, there are no fires that need to be fought." Tony walked to the window and looked out, pretending to scan the horizon for smoke.

Susan watched him out of the corner of her eye. "Because if there was a fire," she said wearily, "Jack would be helping to fight it rather than playing *Nintendo*."

"Right you are, my dear," Tony said. "Right, you are. And I see no smoke anywhere."

"Then I guess you've proved your thesis."

"What thesis was that?"

"That there are no fires."

"Yes, indeed," Tony said, taking another puff from his imaginary pipe. "There are certainly no fires at the moment."

For the first time, Susan smiled. "You know I don't like for you to smoke in the house," she said, reaching for the glass of wine.

After she took a sip, she went to the oven and opened the door. The aroma of beef and noodles filled the kitchen.

Deeming his efforts successful, Tony turned to the subject that he knew was causing his wife's distress. "So I'm guessing you had another tough day with Schultzy."

"You could say that. Look in the wastebasket."

Instead, Tony tapped the wastebasket with his foot, producing the unmistakable sound of tinkling glass.

"How'd it happen?"

"When he came home from school, he just went off."

"So you sent him to his room."

"He just screamed the whole time I was cleaning up the mess." In a deep voice, she repeated the words Schultzy had spoken. "I'm gonna burn this motherfuckin' house. I'm gonna burn all you motherfuckers."

Tony took a deep breath and sighed. "No good day today," he said, using one of Eddie's favorite expressions. He kissed her again on the cheek.

"No good day," Susan agreed.

Susan and Tony worked in silence as they finished preparing the evening meal. Just as silently, the rest of the guys gathered around the table. They were upset, too.

Stevie was among the last to enter. "Me hate this," he said, shaking his head. "Me hate this."

Once they began eating, the silence engendered by Schultzy's bad day was replaced with the silence that often accompanies the enjoyment of good food. Only then did the forgotten assignment intrude on Susan's consciousness.

"Oh, shit!" she said, jumping up from the table.

"What?" everyone asked in unison.

"I forgot to pick up Ed!"

For everyone but Susan, the tension dissipated.

"It's his reading day," she explained. "I was supposed to pick him up an hour ago."

Melissa from Videotowne usually drove Eddie to class, but today she was unavailable.

"He'd call us if he needed us," Tony said. "Let's eat. Then I'll drive to Springfield."

Susan glared at him.

"Okay, I'll go get him now," Tony said, making a half-hearted effort to get up.

Susan grabbed her purse and started for the door.

"Remember, he's been living on his own for three years now," Tony called after her. "And he knows our telephone number."

"It's 555-3322," Stevie volunteered.

"How many times does he call us every day, Stevie?" Tony asked.

"Ten," Stevie said, picking a number that wasn't far off the mark.

More bad news, Susan thought. *He hasn't called once today.*

As she raced down U.S. Route 40 on the way to Springfield, she puffed furiously on a cigarette. She smoked it down to nothing, then lit up another. After a few puffs, she threw it out the window and set about the task of calming herself down. "He does know our telephone number," she reminded herself. "555-3322." As she said it again and again, the numbers became a spontaneous incantation, the continued repetition of which helped her compose herself.

She was relieved when she saw Eddie sitting on a bench in front of the student union, engaged in an animated conversation with his tutor, an attractive young woman whose appeal to Eddie was apparent.

Susan spoke first to the student, apologizing for being late.

"That's okay," the coed said. "We've been calling and calling, but you obviously weren't home."

"You were trying to call us?" Susan asked, mystified.

"At least a half-dozen times."

Susan looked at Eddie, who looked down at the ground, trying to suppress a grin.

"What number were you calling, Ed?" Susan asked suspiciously.

"555-332...3," Eddie said. When he looked up, his eyes flashed with mischief.

"But our number is 3 - 3 - 2 - 2." Then it hit her. The misdial was intentional, its purpose being to extend his visit with the pretty young woman.

Eddie laughed out loud. A few seconds later, the coed figured out what had happened too.

CHAPTER THIRTY-SEVEN

Typical of a fine autumn day in Ohio, the sky was so intensely blue and cloud-free that even Eddie noticed it on his way to work. Following his new route, he detoured past the RadioShack toward the vacant lot where Loolooloo told him that the new apartment complex was to be built. He was excited to see a man working to free a huge yellow bulldozer from the constraints that bound it to its trailer. *Big trator,* he thought, even bigger than the one that graded the Auto Zone site. He watched intently as the man fired up the big diesel engine, then maneuvered the bulldozer back and forth across the site.

———

JOHN PETERMAN NOTICED the fine weather too, but his mood was little improved. "At least it ain't gonna rain," he said as he wedged his bulk into the driver's seat of his fully restored 1956 Thunderbird instead of the pickup truck he usually favored.

Since the removable top had been permanently removed, he drove the T-Bird only when rain was out of the question.

As he wove in and out of traffic, Peterman repeatedly dialed his office on his new state-of-the-art car phone, the use of which usually confirmed his sense of self-importance. But his anger was stoked all over again when he repeatedly got a busy signal. He knew why. That goddamn Sam Goodman was gabbing with someone about something that had nothing to do with the construction business. Peterman moved swiftly away from a traffic light, momentarily consoled by the smooth sound of his newly rebuilt transmission as he shifted through the gears. Then he dialed the phone again. This time, he got through.

"Peterman Construction, Goodman speaking," Sam Goodman said cheerfully.

Sam was a carpenter, but he liked to answer the telephone. Whenever he was in the office, he volunteered to fill in for the receptionist so she could take a break. It was a practice she quickly came to encourage.

"Get your goddamn feet off the desk," Peterman barked.

"My feet aren't on the desk," Sam said truthfully. Then he put his feet on the desk, crossed his legs, and leaned back in his chair. With the receiver pinched between his chin and shoulder, he rolled up the sleeves of his work shirt to reveal the POW bracelet that he had worn since the 1970s, sometimes on one wrist and sometimes on the other.

"Guess who I just got a call from," Peterman barked.

"Who?"

"Mrs. Henry. She said you came over and looked at her driveway and told her that we screwed it up. Why did you tell her that? Does it have rocks and shit sticking out?"

"No."

"Then we didn't screw it up."

"A portion of the base was bad, and a section sank."

Sam always ignored Peterman's bullying, concentrating instead on the facts of the matter.

"Maybe it was just Mother Nature having her way," Peterman said. "Did you ever think of that?"

"I did, but I ruled it out."

"From now on, you just stick to hammering nails, or you'll be looking for a new job."

"We don't hammer too many nails anymore, not since the invention of the nail gun," Sam said, smiling. He could give as well as take.

"Fuck you, Goodman."

Peterman hung up, then drove up over a curb and onto the property that would one day be a thirty-six-unit apartment complex.

———

EDDIE DIVERTED his attention from the bulldozer when the red car pulled onto the construction site and skidded to a stop. He watched a very large man struggle to get out of the small car. He looked angry.

Peterman retrieved a yellow construction hat from the trunk and placed it on his head so forcefully that he hurt himself. He took the hat off, threw it on the ground, then picked it up and put in on again.

He *was* mad, Eddie decided.

Although Yellow Hat was far away, Eddie stood very still in the manner of an animal that hoped to go unnoticed by a predator. He watched Yellow Hat intently as he strode across the field. For a moment, Eddie wondered if the big trator would stop.

It did. As Peterman approached, the driver jumped down.

Eddie could tell that Yellow Hat was still angry because he pointed and gestured wildly. He watched as Yellow Hat picked up several stones and hurled them at the driver's feet, causing him to jump backward.

Abruptly, Peterman ended his rant. Then he lifted his gaze and scanned the perimeter, stopping to look directly at Eddie.

Eddie thought Yellow Hat was going to yell at him, but he didn't. Instead, he turned and stalked off.

Eager to share the big news, Eddie ran directly to Radio-Shack. "Big trator move the dirt," he gasped excitedly to Loolooloo.

"I saw it too."

"My play," he said, meaning "place."

Loolooloo didn't understand. "My play?"

"My play," Eddie said again. "I move."

"But you already have a nice place."

"Fuck old play."

CHAPTER THIRTY-EIGHT

Susan always planned something special when one of the guys celebrated a birthday, and Stevie's was coming up. He would be twenty-six. *Wow,* she thought. *We've been doing this for more than ten years now.* She remembered that for Stevie's thirteenth birthday, she gave him a T-shirt that said, "I'm a teenager." He wore it almost continuously until it was little more than a rag. Then, on his eighteenth birthday, Tony took him to the Red Brick Tavern, a historic watering hole on the old National Road just outside of London. Only after they were seated at the bar did they learn that a new law had gone into effect, increasing the drinking age for beer to twenty-one. So three years later, he had his first beer. He didn't like it.

To celebrate Stevie's 26th birthday, Susan took all the guys bowling. When she pulled the old van to a stop in the parking lot of London Lanes, all the doors opened, and the guys poured out. Stevie hurried on ahead, dragging his heavy bowling bag behind him. By the time he got to the desk, he was out of breath.

"Me green," Stevie said to the man the customers of all ages called Willie. He was the proprietor and husband of Loolooloo.

Stevie was born with a heart defect and recently started taking medication.

"You don't look green," Willie said.

"Me out of breath."

"Then you'd be turning blue. Except that I don't think you are."

"It's my birthday."

"Happy Birthday."

"Me want sign on," Stevie said, pointing to the screen at the top of each alley on which the score sheet was projected.

"We use those signs for leagues, to record official scores."

"I'm in a league," Stevie said.

"What league is that?"

"Special Olympics."

Willie chuckled and made a mental note. The Special Olympics represented a potential piece of business of which he was unaware. "Where do you usually bowl?"

"Springfield."

"What's your handicap?"

Stevie was instantly indignant. "Me not handicapped!" He picked up his bowling bag. "Me go," he said as Susan arrived.

"I didn't mean that kind of handicap," Willie said to Susan as much as to Stevie. "I meant, like, how many pins do you get?"

"Willie is talking about a different kind of handicap," Susan said. "If you're not such a good bowler..."

"Me good bowler!"

"And even good bowlers get to add pins to their score. It makes things more even, more fun."

"Look, Stevie," Willie said, pointing to the lane where the

guys would be bowling. "I turned the sign on. Now it's just like all the people who bowl in leagues."

Mollified, Stevie left to put on his bowling shoes.

"Don't feel bad," Susan said to Willie. "He gets mad at me if I try to park in a handicap space."

After the guys started bowling, Susan stood in the back and watched as Jack did his best to keep score while Larry Little provided commentary and imagined himself to be Harry Spilman. "Stevie is very happy," she said to Eddie, who had bowled two frames before joining her in the back. "If his smile was any bigger, it would crack his face." She was surprised, then, when a feeling of sadness intruded on the moment. She searched for its cause and soon found it. For the first time, she was aware that her time with the guys was coming to an end.

CHAPTER THIRTY-NINE

I n the weeks after the bulldozer completed its job, more and more workers reported to the construction site. Sam Goodman was among them. While many of Sam's fellow workers were not interested in anything beyond the end of their boots, Sam always took a few moments to survey his surroundings. During the first moments of his first day, he spotted Eddie standing at the edge of the site. On the second day, when Eddie took up a position a few feet closer, Sam noticed that too. During a break, Sam motioned for Eddie to come over.

"My new play," Eddie said.

"What?"

"My new play. I move."

"You're gonna live here?"

"Yeah, yeah."

Later, when Sam turned around to pick up his saw, he was surprised that Eddie was waiting to hand it to him. And when Sam lined up the saw with the pencil mark on the board, Eddie shook his head in disapproval. "No, no," he said.

But Sam made the cut, anyway. By less than an inch, the board was too short.

The next day, Sam gave Eddie a pair of boots and a hard hat with the company logo on it. "Your part of the crew, now," Sam said.

Every day thereafter, Eddie roamed freely about the site dispensing advice along the way. Many were surprised to find that Eddie's keen eye helped them avoid mistakes, too. His warnings, unheeded in the beginning, were soon welcomed. More than one feigned a mistake in Eddie's presence to verify for themselves his ability.

But in spite of Eddie's many talents, one worker saw only his deficits.

"Hey, stupid!" the man yelled at Eddie one morning.

Eddie hesitated before he turned around, unsure that the man was speaking to him.

"Yeah, I'm talking to you," the man said. "Make yourself useful and get me a pack of cigarettes."

Eddie stood rigid and speechless.

"Over there, ree-tard," the man said, pointing to his truck.

Sam quickly intervened. "Get 'em yourself," he said curtly.

"I wasn't talking to you."

"But I'm talking to you."

Sam was prepared to let the matter drop, but Eddie wasn't. Later, he loosened the bolts on the front and rear bumpers of the man's pickup truck so that when the man backed out of his parking space at the end of the day, both bumpers fell to the ground, the rear bumper assuming the shape of a pretzel when he drove over it. First, the man examined the pretzel, then the undamaged bumper. As he groped for an explanation, he spotted Eddie standing nearby.

"Yeah," Eddie said. "Good."

Because more people congregate in the parking lot at quitting time than at any other time, a large audience witnessed what happened next. They saw the man start out after Eddie, then draw himself quickly to a halt. And they knew why. Maybe Eddie had a disability, but he could handle himself; they could tell.

Abruptly, the man returned to his truck. He kicked the crumpled bumper out of the way and threw the good one in the back of his truck. Then he swore at Eddie and drove off.

Eddie smiled placidly in return, glad to be a man among men.

CHAPTER FORTY

Cadillac Jack parked his dump truck under the loading shoot at the local gravel pit, then chewed absently on a toothpick as a full load of gravel filled the dump box. As the truck swayed gently, he contemplated the selections he would soon pass along to his bookmaker. Gambling crowded out nearly everything else in Jack's life with the exception of the constant ache of an arthritic hip, one that the doctors told him needed to be replaced but which, owing to a lack of health insurance, never would be. Like many gamblers, Jack struggled to pay his bills, his primary asset being an aging Cadillac Eldorado which he purchased second or third hand from its previous owner. On the driver's side door, he painted in gold lettering the sobriquet of his own invention: "Cadillac Jack."

Jack's preoccupation with his gambling and his hip left him with only a meager reserve of mental energy for other endeavors, like, for instance, his job. Fortunately for Jack, his job was not demanding. After he collected a load of gravel, he dumped it where he was told. Today, he would head for the new apartment complex being built by the Peterman Construction Company.

––––––

John Peterman pulled his T-Bird into the parking lot and skidded to a stop. He pried himself out of his car, thumped the yellow hard hat onto his head, then stomped off to spread his morning dose of ill will.

Nearby, Eddie wandered about the job-site bantering with his new friends. He updated them on the progress of the new Auto Zone, and he discussed the attributes of the new Dodge pickup truck, even though no one believed him when he said that he planned to buy one and learn how to drive it. But when he passed through an almost completed section of the project that was devoid of workers, he noticed a problem that his colleagues had overlooked. When he tried to open an exterior door on one of the units, the door scraped against the wooden deck. It was a problem he thought he could fix.

Wearing his new hard hat and equipped with his new tool belt, he first attempted to elevate the door's swing path, but when that didn't work, he embarked upon a more unconventional plan. He cut a hole in the deck. He did so with the intention of nailing pieces of lumber to the bottom of the hole, thus solving the problem. He was proceeding to Step Two when he was interrupted.

To Eddie's credit, when Peterman pushed on the door, it swung open freely. But when Peterman stepped forward, he plunged four feet into the crawl space below. Dazed, he jumped up before he surveyed the space available to do so. When he did, he hit his head and fell back on his butt. Gazing up at the circle of light above him, he saw the downward-looking face of a redheaded man who looked somehow familiar. When finally, Peterman hoisted himself into an upright position, the top half of his body projected through the hole in the deck so that he was looking at Eddie, eye to eye.

Eddie was the first to break the ice. "Oomp," he said.

Peterman lunged forward and swiped Eddie's feet out from underneath him, knocking him to the deck. Then he grabbed and twisted a leg, trying to remove the boot as Eddie squirmed and banged his arm on the deck like a professional wrestler seeking an outlet for his pain. When the boot didn't yield, Peterman worked his way up Eddie's anatomy. He quickly regretted the tactic. Eddie bit him.

Peterman screamed in pain and released his grip, whereupon Eddie rolled over, scrambled to his feet, and ran. Holding his hard hat with one hand and his tool belt with the other, he ran all the way to the parking lot, where he stopped to catch his breath. As he stood bent over at the waist with his hands on his knees, he became aware of the throaty sound of a diesel engine. Looking around, he noticed for the first time a large dump truck approaching with a load of gravel. With an air of authority enhanced by his official attire, he stood in the middle of the road and waved the truck to a stop. Then, taking a position so that the driver could see him in his rearview mirror, he motioned for the driver to follow his lead as he walked backward into the parking lot.

Inside his truck, Cadillac Jack smiled at his good fortune, thinking that his hip would be spared the punishment that occurred every time he got up or down out of his truck. The Red T-Bird that he saw in his review mirror was another good omen. A long shot named Little Red Bird was entered in the seventh race at Beulah Park, a Columbus area race track. His luck was changing; he could tell.

Now out of his hole, John Peterman broke into a run. "Not there," he screamed. "Not there!"

Peterman started off at a stunning pace, but he tired quickly. Halfway to his destination, his run became a stagger, his scream a wheeze. Instead of waving his hands above his head, he held them out in front of him, preparing himself for the moment when his stagger evolved involuntarily into a crawl.

Cadillac Jack was perplexed. In receipt of conflicting directives from each end of his truck, the proximity of the T-Bird failed any longer to register itself in his consciousness. Reflexively, he submitted to the direction of the little man providing such authoritative guidance.

For his part, Eddie struggled to control the muscles that wanted to arrange his face into a grin. He raised his hands over his head, then signaled for the driver to stop and dump his load.

Slowly, the T-Bird disappeared beneath a full load of gravel. Only when the box was lowered to its bed did Cadillac Jack turn his attention again to the large man in the yellow hard hat who was crawling in his direction. The man looked to be in need of medical attention, Jack thought, but he knew that others would be better equipped than he to provide it.

CHAPTER FORTY-ONE

Because Eddie knew from experience that a period of recrimination often followed one of his misadventures, he had long ago mastered the art of "lying low." During such periods when investigations were conducted and various consequences debated, he was a model of good behavior. Such was the case following the Peterman debacle. Everyone who knew Eddie noticed in him a sudden dedication to his own self-improvement. Loolooloo observed an affinity for aftershave and deodorant, and Susan noticed that dirty dishes no longer collected in his kitchen sink. And when they offered Eddie advice, he accepted it rather than rejecting it out of hand as he usually did.

"He's becoming so... responsible," Loolooloo exclaimed, searching for the appropriate accolade.

"I've seen this before," Susan said. "He's probably done something to somebody. If he gets in trouble, he's hoping that we'll come to his defense and say that he's turned over a new leaf."

But to Eddie's surprise, he emerged from the Peterman

incident unscathed. After two weeks passed, during which he was neither reprimanded nor questioned by "the law," he decided that the danger had passed. Although he no longer visited the construction site, his run-in with Peterman did not diminish his desire to move into the new complex. One afternoon after he got off work, he reestablished contact with the rental agent, a woman of Susan's approximate age, who Eddie recognized as a friend of Fireman Mike.

"I haven't seen you for weeks," the agent said. "I thought maybe I scared you off."

Eddie didn't know how to respond to the agent's banter, so he didn't. Instead, he unfolded a brochure from the stack on the counter and pointed to an artist's rendering of the new complex. "My play," he said, tapping his finger on the unit nearest to the RadioShack.

"Still got your heart set on that one, eh?"

Eddie extracted a rumpled application from his pocket and laid it on the counter.

"Who helped you fill this out?"

"Susan."

"She did a good job," the woman said. "All I need now is your security deposit."

Eddie dug into his pocket and produced a check. But before he handed it over, he drew a line through Susan's signature. Laboriously, he signed his name above it.

For several weeks, Eddie had been demanding control of his checkbook. To protest Susan's lack of action, he always crossed out her signature and replaced it with his own, a practice that the bank had so far not rejected.

If the agent found this odd, she didn't say so. She accepted the check.

On moving day, Eddie borrowed a dolly from Loolooloo and hauled box after box to his new apartment. Among the first items that he unpacked was a new blue vinyl waterbed. He connected the mattress to a garden hose, resisting for the moment the allure of the smooth vinyl surface. Then he left to retrieve additional boxes from his old place. When he got back, he was surprised to see that a crowd had gathered in front of his apartment. He soon discovered why. A stream of water flowed from beneath the front door.

"Did ya bust somethin' already?" someone asked him.

Eddie elbowed his way toward the door with his head down as he fumbled for his keys.

"The building manager ain't gonna like this," someone else said.

Eddie was thinking the same thing, but before he could close the door, several of his neighbors forced themselves through the opening and followed the trail of water into the bedroom. No one was prepared for what they saw, including Eddie. Everyone stood speechless in the presence of a bloated and hissing blob.

"Oh, my God," one person said at last.

"What is it?" asked another.

Slowly and en masse, the group tried to back out of the room.

But it was too late.

When the thing burst, a wall of water caught the retreating observers at the back of the knee, knocking one poor woman to the floor. After they scrambled to safety, one neighbor left to report the incident to the apartment manager while the others waited outside to see what happened next.

Glad to be alone, Eddie slogged across the wet carpeting and locked the front door. Then he turned off the water and closed the blinds. But as he was assessing the damage, he heard the sound of an approaching siren. He returned to the window and peeked out in time to see Officer Brad climb out of his car.

"Anybody inside?" the officer asked.

"A retarded guy with red hair," someone said.

Officer Brad relaxed. Maybe there had been an explosion, and maybe there hadn't. With less urgency, he knocked on Eddie's door.

"Go home, now!" Eddie shouted.

"Open the door, Red."

Eddie opened the door. "Hate the law," he said under his breath as Officer Brad walked in.

Finding the burst waterbed but no evidence of a crime, Officer Brad quickly concluded that the less he knew about this, the better. "If I were you, Red, I'd clean this mess up as quick as I could," he said. Then he left.

The next morning, Eddie folded up the damaged mattress and tried to put it back in the box. When it wouldn't fit, he wrapped it with duct tape. After he located the receipt from a filing system that was understood only by him, he took the mattress back to the store where he bought it, hoisting it with great effort onto the customer service desk.

The woman behind the counter was dumbfounded by the appearance of the "package" in front of her. "What the hell is that?"

"Wa-bed," Eddie said. "Bad wa-bed." He dug into his pocket and extracted a receipt.

The woman poked cautiously at Eddie's package. Apparently satisfied that the object was what Eddie said it was, she was struck next by a thought that should have been obvious but somehow was not. "Are you trying to return that?"

"My mimi back," Eddie said.

"You can't bring that back!" Again she poked at the

package as if to demonstrate that a heretofore animate object was now dead.

"Mimi back," he said again. "One nine five dollar."

"It's damaged beyond repair!"

But Eddie detected the first faint whiff of capitulation in the woman's voice. He pointed to the price as it appeared on the receipt. "One nine five, little dot, three eight dollar," he said, this time adding the cents.

The clerk summoned her supervisor, who summoned the store manager, but Eddie pretended that he couldn't understand any of them. Eventually, the whole group gave up, and Eddie left happily, money in hand.

CHAPTER FORTY-TWO

After Eddie moved to London, Susan repeatedly tried to "cut the apron strings," but she couldn't. She worried about him constantly and checked up on him continually. When Eddie moved to his new apartment, she tried again. *Eddie is a man,* she told herself. *So treat him like one.*

Her plan was to visit him just once a month, but after a week, she manufactured a reason to stop by his apartment. Then the following week, she had a premonition that something terrible had happened, so she rushed over in a panic. And the process of "cutting the apron strings" started all over again.

Today she found herself in her car on the outskirts of London when she realized that she was driving toward his apartment. A few minutes later, she stood at Eddie's front door. But although her index finger was extended in front of the doorbell, she didn't push it. Something was different. She looked to the left. She looked to her right. "That's it!" she exclaimed. While the doors to the apartments on either side of

Eddie's were plain, Eddie's was ornate, featuring leaded glass with beveled edges.

Susan rang the doorbell, and Eddie answered it immediately, leaving her with the impression that he had been observing her approach. She could tell that Eddie was glad to see her, and their smiles lit up the stoop.

"New door," Eddie said proudly.

"I see that," Susan said, resisting the temptation to ask why he thought he needed it.

"New back door," Eddie said. "New shower door too."

"Great," Susan said, meaning the opposite. But suddenly, she had a different concern. Behind Eddie, it looked like it was snowing. "What's going on in there?"

Eddie laughed and stood aside so that Susan could come in and see for herself.

By the time she got to the kitchen, the floor was covered with small feathers. A new washer and dryer stood along one wall.

"What's that?" she blurted needlessly.

"New water dryer," Eddie said, meaning washer and dryer. "Dark brown." He reached into the dryer and pulled out the remnants of a down pillow.

"How are you going to pay for it?" Susan asked amid raining feathers.

"All paid," Eddie exclaimed in a high-pitched voice brimming with excitement. "Mine!"

"But I have the checkbook," Susan said, digging through her purse and holding up the evidence.

Eddie laughed, and his eyes were full of mischief.

"Let me see the receipt," she commanded.

Happily, Eddie showed it to her.

"May I use your phone?"

Eddie brought her a cordless phone. "New phone too."

"I see that."

After she found the bank's phone number, she called and spoke to a representative to find out how much money was in their joint account.

Eddie watched Susan's face intently, waiting for the change in her expression that would reveal the news even before she spoke a word.

"What do you mean, 'less than ten dollars'?" Susan blurted. "I have the checkbook in front of me. We didn't write a check." Then she put her hand over the receiver and glared at Eddie. "It's not funny."

Months earlier, Susan partially acceded to Eddie's long-standing desire to assume control of his checkbook, agreeing that henceforth both of them would sign all checks. Together, they went to the bank and signed new signature cards to confirm the deal. Now, as Susan talked to the banker, she learned what Eddie had discovered some weeks before. Rather than changing the account so that both signatures were required, the account was changed so that either signature was sufficient.

"You think you're pretty smart, don't you?" she said to Eddie after she hung up.

"Yeah," Eddie said, eyes dancing.

The mistake would have remained undiscovered by most customers, but Eddie Fugate was not an ordinary customer. Just as he could instantly spot a dent in a new car or see that a piece of lumber was too short, so too was he quick to identify and exploit the bank's error. During a solo visit to the bank, he discovered that when he asked the teller for money, she gave it to him.

"Do you want cash or a bank check?" the teller had asked him helpfully.

"Mimi," Eddie said calmly. "Twenty-dollar. Not a lot."

On subsequent visits, Eddie returned with price quotations, first from the building supply store and then from the local appliance store. "Bank check," he said each time as he presented a new quote to a teller. Soon he was the proud owner of three new doors, a dark brown washer and dryer, and a cordless telephone.

In the days that followed the discovery of his shopping spree, Eddie maintained his customary low profile. It was an unnecessary precaution, as it turned out since everyone–including Eddie–was surprised at what Susan did next. It wasn't his name that she removed from the account; it was hers.

When Susan told Tony what she had done, he just shook his head.

"You weren't in all those meetings about living your dream," she told him.

"Maybe you're right," Tony said doubtfully. "If he feels more accountability, maybe he won't play games with the bank."

"Do you believe that?"

"No."

Before Susan gave Eddie the checkbook, she talked to him about the magnitude of the responsibility he was assuming. He listened closely, as he always did when he knew he was about to get what he wanted. He professed to understand when Susan explained that money must be deposited *in* the bank before it can be taken *out* of the bank. And when she asked him to collect his bills and put them in a basket on the kitchen counter, he said that he would.

"When you're a man, you pay your bills," she said.

"Yeah, yeah."

Susan came over twice a month to help Eddie write checks. (She always phrased it that way. "Writing checks" was fun.

"Paying bills" was not.) After she had filled in all the necessary information, Eddie signed the check. He did so willingly except for the electric bill, which was always saved for last, with the unfortunate result that the check-writing sessions sometimes ended on a sour note. Otherwise, Susan thought the new system was working.

It wasn't.

During the first week, Eddie tried to buy a new Dodge Hemi pickup truck, but the salesman knew him and refused to accept his check. Unfazed, Eddie turned his attention to a more modest acquisition. He started shopping for a stand-alone freezer.

Paradoxically, at the same time, Susan granted Eddie more responsibility; she also monitored his activities more closely than ever. She checked regularly with Loolooloo at Radio-Shack, Clyde at Goodyear Chrysler Plymouth, and Melissa at Videotowne to see if they had observed any evidence that Eddie was not behaving responsibly.

"He's talking a lot about buying a freezer," Loolooloo said.

Melissa confirmed it.

Susan confronted Eddie immediately.

"Let me see your checkbook."

Eddie handed it to her.

"You wrote some checks," she said, disgusted. "What for?"

Eddie said nothing.

"Did you save the receipts?"

"Oomp," he said, hitting his forehead with the palm of his hand.

Because she saw no point in arguing, Susan wrote a check out for the monthly rent. Then she gave it to Eddie for him to sign. "Where's your telephone bill?"

"No come."

"How about the other bill?"

The electric bill was never referred to by name.

Eddie said nothing.

"If you don't pay your bills, you know what will happen."

"No," Eddie said. His eyes danced.

"You'll get evicted."

"No!"

"Ed, honey," she said. "You just can't make all the choices. Sometimes we have to do stuff we don't like to do."

"No!"

With that, Susan left. "Screw this empowerment shit," she told Tony when she got home. "It's not gonna work."

The next day, she went to the bank, closed Eddie's account, and opened a new one in her name only. Then she went to Eddie's apartment and told him what she had done. When she asked Eddie to give her the checkbook, he refused.

After Susan left, Eddie stood in the middle of the living room and rocked back and forth. "Fuck you, Susan," he said again and again. Gradually, he dissipated his excess energy, and the rocking slowed and then stopped. Sadly, he retrieved his now useless checkbook. Slowly and methodically, he tore checks individually from the checkbook and laid them on the counter in a neat pile. One by one, he cut the unused checks into confetti, then watched forlornly as they fell like rain into the wastebasket.

CHAPTER FORTY-THREE

"It's gonna take me longer to find a parking place than it did to drive to Springfield," Tony said, disgusted.

According to the article in the *Springfield News-Sun*, Bill Clinton was scheduled to start speaking thirty minutes ago.

"Too many cars," Jack said.

Tony pulled into the parking lot behind the Presbyterian Church and looked at his watch. They still had a ten-minute walk across downtown.

"We're gonna miss him, aren't we?" Jack said.

"No, we're not gonna miss him. Bill Clinton is never on time."

Tony was right. The Arkansas Governor's campaign plane was still on the runway in Pittsburgh.

For weeks, polls had shown Clinton with a double-digit lead over both President George H. W. Bush and third-party challenger Ross Perot. But in the final days of the campaign, Clinton's lead had shrunk, and both Bush and Clinton were now focusing efforts on a few key states in the South and

Midwest. Two days before, at a rally in Columbus, President Bush claimed with bravado that "The Big Mo" was now his. Perhaps fearful that he was right, Bill Clinton tonight would make his third trip to Ohio.

Tony pulled his coat tight around his neck to protect himself against the forty-degree weather. Jack did the same. Tony thrust his hands deep into his pockets. So did Jack. Then the two of them started to walk, Jack perfectly mimicking Tony's gait.

"Who are you gonna vote for?" Jack asked.

"I don't know," Tony said.

Actually, he did know, but he wanted Jack to make up his own mind. In four days, Jack would vote in his first presidential election.

"Who are you gonna vote for?" Tony asked.

"I don't know either."

On the far side of the four-story brick and limestone building that once housed the city offices, opera house, and downtown market, a crowd of 10,000 people huddled in the gathering darkness. Built in 1890, the hulking Romanesque structure filled an entire block, providing an impressive backdrop to the speakers' platform. A half-block away on the City Plaza, the sponsors of Jaycee's annual "Fright Night" Halloween party instructed the rock-n-roll band to cease playing at the first sign of an arriving motorcade. In a similar spirit of cooperation, administrators at nearby South High School rerouted the annual homecoming parade so that the marching band wouldn't compete with the candidate. Further away, Conrail officials delayed the freight train that usually rumbled through the downtown at this hour.

Tony and Jack took up a position at the back of a crowd, and Tony hoisted Jack onto his shoulders so that he could see. But Jack was a man, not a boy.

"Put me down," Jack said. "I'm gonna watch from the platform."

"How are you gonna get up there?"

"I'm gonna make sure Mr. Tackett sees me."

Roger Tackett was a county commissioner. An inveterate campaigner, Commissioner Tackett, always attended the South Vienna Corn Festival. When he did, he sometimes stopped at the group home to chat with the guys who hung out on the porch. He felt a special bond with the guys since he, too, was disabled, having been rendered paraplegic by a sniper's bullet in Viet Nam.

After Jack left, Tony studied the scene in front of him. A few Bush-Quayle signs protruded politely from the crowd, and a few more GOP supporters stood on the balcony of the downtown hotel. The speakers' platform was filled with local and state Democratic politicians, including Senator John Glenn, who would win a fourth term the following Tuesday.

Just as the lights of the motorcade became visible in the distance, Jack talked his way onto the dais. Commissioner Tackett was glad to see him.

After a too-long series of introductions, Bill Clinton got right to the point. Recalling that President George Bush the day before referred to Clinton and Gore as "crazy extremists," Clinton made the theme his own.

"I'll tell you what I think is crazy," he said. "I think it's crazy that unemployment is up and incomes are going down. I think it's crazy that a guy who said, 'Read my lips,' signed the second biggest tax increase in history and is now campaigning as somebody against taxes. I think it's crazy that there are more poor people now than there were four years ago. I think it's crazy that 100,000 Americans a month are losing their health insurance."

Then he told the cheering crowd what he would do differently. He promised health care for all Americans. He promised a college education in return for community service. He promised to balance the budget and restore the economy. Finally, he appealed to Ohio's farmers. "Al Gore lives on a farm," he said. "When it comes to farming, Bush and Quayle don't know come here from sic 'em."

———

ON ELECTION DAY, Jack Runkle got up very early in the morning. He left his apartment across the street from the fire department and walked by Shoemaker's Market and the group home, neither of which showed signs of activity. He strode purposefully to his assigned polling place, the South Vienna Elementary School. When he came out, he wore his badge of honor proudly. "I voted," the sticker on his lapel said. And so, too, would it be announced every day thereafter until the decal was so filthy and unrecognizable that Susan finally scraped it off his jacket.

CHAPTER FORTY-FOUR

Susan sat on her butt in the hallway outside of Schultzy's bedroom, exhausted but not sleepy. She took another sip of coffee and another drag on her cigarette. Tony once told her that when he was in the Navy, he could smoke a whole pack of cigarettes during a midwatch, the four-hour period after midnight. If it wasn't 4:00 a.m., it was close to it, and she figured she'd smoked at least a pack. She lifted her chin upward as she exhaled and pressed her shoulders against the wall. Behind her, all was quiet.

But not for long. With his bare hands, Schultzy separated another piece of molding from the wall. The wood splintered with a loud crack that made Susan jump. She jumped again when Schultzy hurled the piece of wood across the room. And she shuddered as he repeated in a deep satanic voice what he was going to do to the house and all the people in it.

A short time later, Tony got up to relieve her, but she sent him back to bed. "I couldn't go to sleep now if I tried," she said.

Tony arose again at dawn. When he did, Susan called the emergency squad. The crew placed Schultzy in restraints and transported him to the inpatient psychiatric unit attached to one of Springfield's two hospitals. After Schultzy was admitted, Susan quickly returned home so she could shower and compose herself in time for a long-scheduled visit from a man representing the State of Ohio.

Weeks before, when Susan and Tony realized that Schultzy needed more care than they could provide, Susan began the search for another placement. First, she called the Springview Developmental Center in Springfield, a facility built originally as a tuberculosis hospital, then eventually acquired by the State and converted into an institution for adults with severe physical and intellectual disabilities. But after the briefest of meetings, the admitting officer politely refused to accept Schultzy, citing an inability to deal with mental illness. Next, Susan tried to place Schultzy at the Mueller Center, a residential program in Springfield established to ensure that the county's citizens with intellectual disabilities would always be provided for locally. But the official reminded Susan that Schultzy was originally from another county and, therefore, not eligible. So Susan called Schultzy's mother. She joined the search, focusing her efforts on facilities nearer her home. But nobody wanted Schultzy. Unable to find another placement, Tony set up a meeting to ask for the additional funding that would be needed to hire more staff. That was the meeting Susan rushed home to prepare for.

The meeting went badly from the start. As Susan described the various episodes that occurred during the previous month, the man flipped absently through the pages of Schultzy's file, concentrating most of his effort on the cheeseburger that he brought with him.

After Susan finished, the man brushed some crumbs off the page and closed the folder. "Just by reading the notes, he doesn't seem that bad," he said.

"Then let's go upstairs and look at what's left of his room," Tony said.

"You missed my point."

"I think you missed mine," Tony replied, moving to the edge of his seat.

But Susan held up her hand and waved him off. "So, are you telling us that our request won't be approved?"

"If it isn't documented, it didn't happen," he said dismissively. Then he burped.

"Then that's it," Susan said. "We quit." She slouched in her chair.

Tony's jaw dropped, and his anger turned to amazement. Suddenly, the man from the State was merely an unwanted caller who needed to be dispatched. Tony walked to the front door and held it open. "Thanks for coming," he said.

A decision that he had advocated for two years was made in an instant. "It's the right thing to do," Tony said after they were alone. "Both for Christopher and for us. And for the guys."

"It's not good for anyone to live like this," Susan said.

But there was more to it than that. While Susan and Tony had tried to create an environment that was different from institutions like Orient, she now saw the similarities. "You just can't put large groups of people with disabilities together in one place and think that they will develop up to their capacities, no matter how much you put into it," she told Tony.

Later that afternoon, someone from the hospital called to say that Schultzy was ready to come home. "We're not picking him up," Susan said. "We're getting out of the business."

During the next few months, Susan and Tony found placements for the guys that remained. Several returned to their home communities, including Stevie, who moved to a foster home near his father. Billy, the sweet young man with the fewest abilities, moved in with his sister. Larry Little, the sports announcer and Eddie's longstanding antagonist, moved to the apartment next to Jack. And Kevin, his sexual orientation now firmly established, traveled with a newfound friend to Florida, where he got a job working on a cruise ship.

As for Schultzy, he was moved to an apartment in Springfield where he lived alone with round-the-clock staff at a cost of $140,000 per year. He was never the same again, the pattern of a few good days sandwiched between the bad replaced by a state of perpetual dullness.

After everyone was placed, Susan and Tony sold the group home to a man who hoped to turn it into a bed-and-breakfast. Tony went to work full-time as a probation officer, and Susan, burned out and exhausted, took a job as a waitress at a restaurant in Columbus.

Meanwhile, Schultzy's mother continued her efforts to bring her son home. Several years later, she succeeded, and Schultzy was moved to a foster home near her. But after a week, the foster parents quit, and Schultzy was returned to the same institution from which his mother had worked so hard to arrange his escape.

CHAPTER FORTY-FIVE

Susan took the job as a waitress because she thought she needed a break from social service work, but she hated it. She was accustomed to being on her feet, so that part didn't bother her. But because she was a tall woman, she bent over a lot, which made her back hurt all the time. Plus, too many customers were just plain rude. "It wouldn't hurt to thank your waitress every once in a while," she told Tony one evening.

As it happened, her employment lasted only a few weeks. She quit on the day that Jack Runkle died. He was 28 years old.

The week before, Tony and Susan completed the purchase of a new home on Lake Choctaw, a manmade lake between London and South Vienna. On Tony's last trip to South Vienna, he stopped at Jack's apartment to say goodbye. He found Jack on the sofa with a game of *Nintendo* filling the television screen. He had died during a seizure.

Susan made arrangements with the funeral home in London while the men at the Harmony Township Fire Department organized the church service. Three days later, friends and coworkers gathered in the sanctuary of the South Vienna Community Church for a service filled with music, prayer, and fond remembrances. Except for Schultzy and Kevin, all the guys from the group home came back for the service.

Afterward, Tony and Stevie talked about the life they had shared with Jack.

"He was a good man," Tony said.

"Bossy," Stevie replied.

It was true. Jack viewed himself as a cut above the rest of the guys, probably because he was the only one who had attended public school and learned to read. As a result, he exuded an air of superiority, especially when he took it upon himself to use his best Tony impersonation to admonish the other guys for even minor infractions of house rules. When Stevie was the one being censored, a wrestling match usually followed.

But then Stevie put his relationship with Jack into a perfect perspective. "I didn't like Jack," he said. "But I loved Jack."

For Eddie, Jack's death was a concrete representation of his own mortality. "Jack in the dirt now," he said to Susan.

"Jack's gone to heaven," Susan said.

"I no go in the dirt."

"We'll all die sometime."

"Not me," Eddie said. "Stay home."

The toughest part for Susan came after Jack was buried. Partly because it was in her make-up and partly because she had nothing else to do, Susan blamed herself for Jack's death. "If I'd been around, I would've seen it coming," she said.

Tony proceeded cautiously. "Remember the day Jack had a seizure when he was climbing over the outfield fence to retrieve a baseball?"

"Of course."

"You thought you could keep him safe by convincing him

not to play baseball. But you realized that it was such an important part of his life."

"No, I didn't. I just realized I couldn't make him quit playing." But because she was prolonging a conversation that she didn't want to have, she acceded to Tony's point. "You're right. He still had to live his life."

"He died playing *Nintendo*," Tony said. "There wasn't anything he loved doing more than that."

When Susan remained mired in her funk, Tony took her to see the psychiatrist who treated Eddie. When he couldn't help, he took her to see their former back-door neighbor, Henrietta Hocter, the South Vienna mayor. For several hours, Susan sat at Henrietta's kitchen table, and the two women talked.

Henrietta said many of the things that Tony had already said. She told Susan that it was the way that Jack would have wanted to go, that he didn't suffer, and that it was the way it was meant to be. But at that time and at that place, it was Henrietta Hoctor who unconditionally embraced Susan's right to grieve without trying to minimize it or tell her how it was that she ought to feel.

After a while, Susan got around to saying what it was that was most on her mind. "I feel like it's my fault that he's dead."

Henrietta grasped Susan's hand between both of hers. And when Susan looked at her, she saw a face that was filled with kindness and love and the simple wisdom that comes with living a long life.

"You know that's not true, child," Henrietta said.

It was the beginning of peace in Susan's mind.

"You know something else, too," Henrietta said.

Susan waited to find out what else it was that she knew.

"Everyone *knew* Jack," Henrietta said. "The fireman knew Jack. The neighbors knew Jack. All the folks at Shoemaker's Market knew Jack."

"Not to mention everyone in town who buys lottery tickets," Susan said, forcing herself not to dwell on the fact that the amount of money Jack spent on lottery tickets was just one more thing she had worried about.

Together the two women sat in silence, reviewing in their minds the list of all the people who knew Jack.

"Even the players from Jack's old baseball team came back," Susan said at last.

"Jack had friends," Henrietta said. Then she hesitated long enough to make sure that she had Susan's complete attention. "You did that, Susan."

"He lived a wonderful life," Susan said.

It was as close as she would come to acknowledging the tribute that she had been paid.

"So let's celebrate it," Henrietta said. "And not worry about what might have been."

———

SEVERAL MONTHS LATER, the formal celebration of Jack's life was concluded at the annual banquet of the Harmony Township Fire Department. In a brief ceremony, the chief unveiled a plaque onto which the name of Fire Recruit Second Class Jack Runkle had been engraved. During the previous year, the chief noted, Jack had completed twenty-one hours of training and made fifteen fire runs.

CHAPTER FORTY-SIX

1998

Eddie Fugate gripped the steering wheel tightly with both hands, then eased the car onto U.S. Route 40, accelerating slowly until his speed approached forty miles per hour. He held fast to the right side of the right lane and focused his full attention on the road ahead. But when he heard the deep growl of a diesel engine behind him, he looked in the rearview mirror. Locking his eyes for a moment too long on the eighteen-wheeler that was gaining on him, the car edged onto the gravel berm. Eddie jerked the wheel, and the car fishtailed back onto the pavement.

"Forget about the truck," Guy Thompson said. "Just pay attention to what's happening in front of you."

Guy Thompson's real name was Reggie Ferguson, but when Eddie tried to pronounce it, "Guy Thompson" was what came out. Now many of Reggie's friends called him Guy Thompson too—never just "Guy," but always "Guy Thompson."

Guy Thompson reached up and adjusted the mirror so that

he could monitor what was happening behind them. "I'll watch the truck," he said. "You keep the car on the road."

The section of U.S. Route 40 on which they were driving ran alongside Interstate 70, so it was lightly traveled. Most of the few trucks that did use the road were associated with a truck driving school run by the community college in Springfield.

"Bad truck," Eddie said, not looking when it pulled alongside.

"He's learning to drive just like you are," Guy Thompson said.

In the beginning, Eddie drove around the grounds of the Molly Caren Agricultural Center, a nearby facility located on a large tract of land owned by The Ohio State University. Except for a few days in the fall when the center hosted an agricultural trade fair, the grounds were largely deserted. Now a few miles behind them, the center was still the point from which each session commenced.

Again, Eddie drifted into the berm. Once more, he jerked the car back onto the highway.

"That's what you've got to work on," Guy Thompson said. "You're over-correcting." He held up his hands in front of him as if he were gripping a steering wheel, then moved his hands ever so slightly. "The wheel should always be in a state of almost imperceptible movement."

During Eddie's tumultuous years at WeMIB, Guy Thompson ran the wood shop. When Eddie threw the chisel past the supervisor's ear, it was Guy Thompson's ear, past which it whistled. And when Eddie hit his coworker over the head with a broom, Guy Thompson intervened and broke up the fight.

Guy Thompson and Eddie were now friends, not the friendship of the professional and the client, but actual friends.

Guy Thompson was a very democratic man who was oblivious to class distinctions. When he felt a romantic spark between himself and one of the "consumers" he met at the workshop, he pursued a relationship. And when they fell in love, he married her. But when his new wife decided that the workshop rules no longer applied to her, Guy Thompson sprang to her defense. Forced to choose sides, Guy Thompson quit. With time temporarily on his hands, he took up the challenge of teaching Eddie how to drive.

Eddie failed to negotiate a curve in the road, and the car crossed from the right lane into the left, then edged onto the berm on the other side. Eddie jerked the wheel, and the car bounced back onto the highway. In this manner, Eddie drove down Route 40 until they reached Summerford, a little "pike town" between London and South Vienna.

Eddie was thrilled by his accomplishment. "Now drive a truck!

"You haven't learned how to drive a car yet," Guy said. "Plus, you still need to get your learner's permit. Technically, we shouldn't even be doing this."

"Buy new truck," Eddie said, ignoring Guy. "No wear seat belt."

"I know," Guy Thompson said wearily. "And you're going to drink beer and throw the can out the window."

Eddie laughed.

But Guy wasn't finished. "You know you're going to have to start taking the test again. How many years has it been?"

After a short silence, Eddie said, "No read."

"Maybe that's because you never went to see the tutor Susan got for you."

"Shut up, Guy."

"I bet she could get you another one."

Eddie was thinking about it; Guy could tell.

But not for long. "Buy truck now," Eddie said, changing the subject.

"Do you know how much a new truck costs?"

Eddie was on firmer ground now. "One, eight, two, two, five, little dot, oh, oh dollars."

"That's probably right, actually," Guy said, surprised. "Eighteen thousand dollars. And how much have you saved so far?"

Eddie was silent.

"Let me guess. You got nothin'."

"Fuck you, Guy Thompson."

"So that's another thing. You better start saving your money," Guy Thompson said. "And I mean lots of money."

CHAPTER FORTY-SEVEN

After Jack died, Susan took a job with an agency in Springfield that served troubled youth. A few years later, she convinced a friend who had taken a literary interest in Eddie to help him with his checkbook. "It won't be that much work," she told the man who knew better but willingly accepted the challenge anyway. With a new job and someone else to help Eddie pay his bills, Susan, at last, took a step back. Maybe the apron strings weren't cut, but they were loosened. She still talked frequently to Eddie, and she dropped by often to visit. And when Eddie had a crisis, she helped him regroup, like after he lost his job at Goodyear Chrysler Plymouth.

Clyde Goodyear knew that the new man who worked in the wash bay with Eddie was teasing him and causing him to get into trouble. Clyde reprimanded the man on several occasions and thought the problem was solved, but it wasn't, as he learned one day when he overheard a conversation.

"Eddie," the man said. "Why don't you pull the next car into the wash bay?"

"Yeah, yeah."

"Oops. I forgot. You don't have a driver's license," the man said, pulling his license out of his wallet and waving it in front of Eddie.

Clyde fired the guy on the spot, but when Eddie's performance continued to deteriorate, Clyde realized that the bullying employee wasn't entirely to blame. Eddie was obsessed with buying a truck and driving it, interrupting salesmen when they were with customers, and badgering Clyde for information about possible new shipments. And whenever a mechanic worked on a pickup truck, Eddie abandoned the wash bay to watch. His new obsession kept him from doing his job during the day, and it kept him from sleeping at night so that when he got to work, if he wasn't talking about trucks, he was complaining about being tired. More than once, he fell asleep in the break room. Clyde tolerated the behavior for as long as he could, but when he began to fear that Eddie's behavior might be hurting sales, he had to fire him.

After Eddie lost his job, Susan helped him look for a new one. Because she believed that he might do better with a routine that was more varied, she found not one new job but several. On Mondays, Eddie cleaned golf carts at the London Country Club. On Tuesdays, he detailed tractors at the John Deere dealership. On Wednesdays, he swept, dusted, and otherwise cleaned the local funeral home, often staying afterward for a lunch that the owner's wife prepared for him. Then on Thursdays, he worked at the second of London's two tractor dealers, the "red trator play," as he called it. After work, Eddie usually stopped at RadioShack to see Loolooloo.

Today, when he stopped at RadioShack, he dispensed with his usual banter. "Need new eyes," he said, rubbing both eyes with his fists.

"What's wrong with your eyes?" Loolooloo asked.

"Eyes bad."

"Look at me," she said.

Knowing that it was hard for Eddie to look another person in the eye consciously, she cradled his chin between her thumb and index finger. With his hands at his sides, Eddie repeatedly squeezed his eyes shut and then opened them wide.

"Your eyes *are* red, but that could just be because you've been rubbing them," Loolooloo said.

"Need new eyes," Eddie said again, making circles with his thumb and index finger and holding them up to his eyes.

"You mean you want *glasses!*" Loolooloo said, finally understanding.

"Yeah, do!"

"You should tell Susan to take you to the eye doctor."

"I do one time!"

"Did he say you needed glasses?"

"No," Eddie said dejectedly.

———

THE NEXT DAY, Eddie walked across town to the office of another optometrist. This time, he achieved his objective. He failed the vision test. When he ordered his glasses, he selected the frames that required the largest possible lenses. Then, on each lens, he requested an engraving. On one lens, he wanted the word "Dodge," and on the other, the word "Hemi."

A week later, he picked up his new glasses and rushed to show Loolooloo.

When she saw him for the first time, she almost dropped her coffee. "I thought the doctor told you that you didn't need glasses."

"See *new* doctor," Eddie said, smiling broadly.

"I've never seen glasses like that," Loolooloo said.

"Big glasses," Eddie said.

"And they look like have writing on them," Loolooloo said.

"Yeah, do," Eddie said.

Loolooloo leaned forward for a better look.

"Dodge Hemi," Eddie said, pointing first to one lens and then to the other.

"I see that now," she said. "It's a very unique look, I have to say."

Eddie laughed happily, glad for the endorsement. "Yeah."

"Do you like the way you look in glasses?"

"Yeah, do."

"Maybe we both look better in glasses." Loolooloo took hers off so Eddie could make a comparison. "What do you think?"

Eddie shrugged. He didn't have an opinion.

"I tried contact lenses once," Loolooloo said as she put her glasses back on. "But then I decided I looked better in glasses."

Eddie was lost.

"Do you know what contact lenses are?"

"No," Eddie said.

"They're like tiny little glasses without frames. They stick right on your eyeballs."

Eddie grimaced and squinted, closing his eyes tightly. "Hate da contacts," he said.

Loolooloo laughed. "I thought I'd get you with that one," she said.

Eddie took his glasses off and let them hang on the thick red cord to which they were affixed. Then he disappeared to the section of the store where the audio equipment was displayed. When he returned with a cassette tape player, Loolooloo learned that the purpose of his visit was only partly to show her his new glasses.

"What do you want with *that*?" Loolooloo asked.

Eddie pulled several small cassette tapes out of his pocket and put them on the counter. "Help me drive," Eddie said.

Loolooloo read the label out loud. "Learning to drive: The rules of the road."

"Yeah, yeah," Eddie said. Then he showed her a box of flashcards, each card depicting a different road sign.

"Where did you get all this stuff?" Loolooloo asked.

"Garage sale."

The next day, Eddie went to the local office supply store and made a down payment on a desk and chair, then paid cash for an assortment of office supplies, including legal pads, manila folders, pens and pencils, and a stapler. Later that evening, he called Susan and asked her to reschedule the reading classes that he had abandoned in frustration several years before.

Within a few weeks, his plan was fully executed. On the afternoons, when he didn't meet with his tutor, he listened to his driving tapes or asked Melissa or Loolooloo to help him review his flash cards. In the evenings, he sat down at his new desk, put on his new glasses, and studied his reading material. On Saturday mornings, he took the written test for his temporary driver's permit.

He always failed.

CHAPTER FORTY-EIGHT

Once, Eddie got a check in the mail. Then, on another occasion, he received a bill that looked like a check, so he endorsed it and took it to the bank. To his delight, an inattentive banker cashed it. Since then, he had eagerly anticipated the delivery of the mail on the off chance that it might contain legal tender.

Now he stood in front of his living room window, rocking back and forth while he waited for the letter carrier to approach the cluster of mailboxes near the entrance to the complex. When the man came into view, Eddie left to meet him, giving a wide berth to the kids on the playground who had been teasing him. But on his way back, he saw that the children were waiting for him. As they ran toward him, screaming in their high-pitched, youthful voices, he bent over with his hands over his ears.

"No! Bad girl! Go now," he yelled. Then he picked up a rock and whistled it over their heads.

But what Eddie meant as a warning shot, the girls saw as a

direct assault. One of them registered a complaint with her mother, who also happened to be the new apartment manager.

A few minutes later, the manager appeared at Eddie's door with her daughter in tow. "Is that the man who threw the rock at you?"

"That's him."

"Don't you ever do that again!" she said, wagging a finger in Eddie's face. "Or I'll throw you out of here so fast your head will spin."

With his attention still focused on the woman, Eddie retrieved a light bulb from an assortment of objects that he kept on a small table beside the front door for just such an occasion. "I throw light bulb," he said, cocking his arm.

"You're crazy!" the apartment manager said, retreating with her daughter to the sidewalk.

The trace of a smile on Eddie's face went unnoticed.

"You watch yourself, buddy!"

"I do it!" Eddie said, this time making a throwing motion without releasing the light bulb.

When the woman took another step back, Eddie threw the light bulb. He laughed as it bounced without breaking on the pavement.

"If I have to call the police, I will," the manager exclaimed.

"Fuck the law!" Eddie said, slamming the door. Then he watched from the window as the woman took her daughter by the hand and scurried off. After she was gone, he retrieved his light bulb and put it back on the little stand by the door.

The next day, Eddie found a piece of paper wedged into the crack between the front doorframe and the storm door. He yanked it out and tried to read it but couldn't, so he called Susan.

When Susan arrived, he rushed out of his apartment and

rocked impatiently by her car while she got out. "Hate da new girl," he said.

"What new girl?"

"I hit girl," Eddie said. "I hurt her."

Eddie often made threats when he was mad, so Susan assumed that he was referring to something he would like to do rather than something that he had done.

"I do it! I throw light bulb."

Susan saw that Eddie had a piece of paper in his hand. "Is that the paper you called me about?"

"New girl put paper in door," Eddie said, handing it to her.

When Susan read the flyer, she was relieved. "All the residents got one of these," she said. "It just says that everyone should keep their patios clean and their trash picked up."

"No!"

"It doesn't say, 'Ed Fugate must keep his patio neat.' It says, '*all* residents.'"

Eddie pointed at the door of one neighbor, then another, and another. "No paper. No paper. No paper," he said.

"By the time you got home from work, the other people had taken their notes down. You are *not* being singled out," Susan said, scanning the doors up and down the complex. "Look, way down there," she said, pointing. "There's another piece of paper sticking out of a door."

"No!"

"You don't want to come home and see a bunch of trash lying in people's backyard, do you?"

"My home!"

For the first time, a thought occurred to Susan. "Is there a new apartment manager?"

"I throw light bulb. I hit girl. I laugh," Eddie said. "Ha, ha."

Susan made a mental note to call the apartment manager and provide her with her telephone number.

After Susan left, Eddie tore up the notice and threw it into the wastebasket, which he then emptied into his trash can. The entire contents of his trash can he dumped on the middle of his patio. Still not satisfied, he collected a few other odds and ends and added them to the pile. In a final flourish, he finished off the container of Hawaiian Punch in his refrigerator and tossed it outside, too. Then he spread the trash evenly across the entire area of the patio and went inside, and called Susan to tell her what he had done.

CHAPTER FORTY-NINE

On Saturdays, after Eddie took his driver's exam, he often walked across the street to the lumber company. If the salesmen were too busy to talk to him, he looked through catalogs to stay abreast of the latest innovations in home improvement. But when he wanted to make a purchase, he was all business, commandeering a salesperson without regard to whether or not he was otherwise occupied. If the purchase was too big to carry, he borrowed a shopping cart and pushed it home. But his most recent purchase was so large that he qualified for free delivery.

Now he stood at the entrance to the apartment complex and waited for the lumber truck to arrive. When it did, he flagged it down and guided the driver to a parking space in front of his apartment. Focused on taking possession of the delivery, he didn't see the apartment manager when she approached.

"What do you think you're doing?" she asked.

"Go now!" Eddie yelled, examining the ground around him as if he were searching for a rock.

The apartment manager took several steps backward, for the first time noticing the size of the load on the back of the truck. "Is all that yours?"

When Eddie laughed but didn't answer, the woman posed her question more civilly to the driver. "Are you unloading all of that stuff here?"

"Most of it," the driver said, manipulating the forklift from the back of the truck. "Stand back, Eddie. I don't want to drop this on your foot."

Like everyone else who worked at the lumber company, the driver knew Eddie Fugate.

A new concern suddenly occurred to the apartment manager, and she returned her attention to Eddie. "What are you going to build?"

Eddie pretended to once more look for a rock.

The manager retreated further. "You're not adding on a deck, are you?"

"No."

"Because if you are, you can't. It's against regulations."

This time, Eddie picked up a rock and watched with amusement as the woman scurried off. Then he returned his attention to the deliveryman. "Where new saw?"

"Oops, sorry," the man said, climbing back up on the truck. He found the box that contained a new circular saw and kicked it over to the edge of the truck, where Eddie could grab it. "Be careful with this."

"Yeah, do."

Inside his apartment, Eddie worked noisily through the night as lights went on and off around the complex. When the next-door neighbor pounded on the wall, Eddie stopped what he was doing and pounded back.

The next morning when the apartment manager arrived for work, she found her answering machine filled with messages from irate residents. Fearing another confrontation, she called Susan. "Your friend is building something," she said. "I think he's adding a deck."

"He's never built one of those before," Susan said, adding to the manager's apprehension.

"You can't add on to an apartment that you are renting! It's against regulations."

"More likely, it's something for the inside. He's been building things all his life."

Many images popped into Susan's head. She recalled the "donk house" he built at Orient and the amazingly functional dresser he constructed for his first apartment. Made out of corrugated cardboard, it was stitched together with coat hangers. And more recently, he had built a bed frame big enough to accommodate the special-order blue-vinyl mattress that he purchased after the debacle with the waterbed.

But Susan didn't mention any of these projects. "He's probably building a safe," she said. "He does that."

Susan told the woman about Eddie's life at Orient and about moving to the group home where, for the first time, he could acquire personal possessions. Because he feared that his belongings would be stolen as they would have been at Orient, he wrapped his storage chest with coils of rope before he left his room. Now, many years later, Eddie still took precautions. He built "safes," sturdy wooden boxes with a door and a lock.

————

BY MID-AFTERNOON, Eddie had completed his project, so he stowed his tools, swept up the sawdust, and stood back to admire the finished product. He pushed the safe to see if it would glide on its big brass castors. It did. Then he tested the door. It swung easily on its heavy-duty hinges. Satisfied, he retrieved a twenty-dollar bill from deep in the bowels of his cardboard dresser. "If you want to buy a truck," Guy Thompson had told him, "You'd better start saving your money—lots of money."

With the seriousness and sense of anticipation that often marks the beginning of a long journey, Eddie carefully laid the twenty-dollar bill in the bottom of the safe. Then he closed the door and locked it.

CHAPTER FIFTY

For most of his life, Eddie lived in spending mode. After he moved into his new apartment, he purchased his waterbed, three new doors, a washer and dryer, and finally, a desk. He also added to his collection of vinyl pillows and started his collection of *American Tourister* luggage, buying only the vintage, hard-backed types that he found at garage sales.

But after he built his safe, Eddie went just as aggressively into saving mode. Except for his weekly meal at the funeral home or the pizzas that Loolooloo bought him, he quit eating lunch. He scrimped on groceries, and he stopped going to garage sales. He also got "new work." With Susan's help, he added a fifth job cleaning the Sheriff's offices on Friday mornings.

When he cashed his paychecks, he always asked for twenty-dollar bills. Every day, he took all of his twenties out of his safe, spread them out across the living room floor, and counted them. He always knew how many he had, even if he didn't know how much they were worth. Today, with the proceeds from two new paychecks, he had 105 twenty-dollar bills.

Outside, Guy Thompson honked his horn.

Eddie secured the stack of twenties with a rubber band and locked it in the safe. Then he slid onto the passenger's seat so that Guy could drive to the place where he would take the wheel.

"Got lotta money now," Eddie said.

"How much?"

"One, oh, five."

Guy Thompson knew that Eddie converted his savings to twenty-dollar bills. "You have 105 twenty-dollar bills?"

"Yeah, yeah."

Guy Thompson did the math. "That's $2,100!"

"Buy truck now."

"I hate to tell ya, but you don't have near enough," Guy Thompson said, not mincing words. He talked to Eddie just like he talked to everyone else. "You probably need eight more stacks of twenties, just like the one in your safe now."

"No!" Eddie ripped the glasses from the cord that held them in place around his neck and threw them out the window.

Guy Thompson braked, turned around, and retrieved the glasses. "If you throw them out the window again, I'm not going back after them."

"Fuck you, Guy Thompson."

Guy knew why Eddie was upset. "Twenty-one hundred dollars *is* a lot of money," he said. "Honestly, it's more money than I have."

But the damage was done.

Guy Thompson tried to change the subject, except that with Eddie, it was hard to find subjects to talk about other than new trucks and driving. He went through a list in his head. He would like to talk about Frank Sinatra's death the previous week, but Eddie didn't know who Frank Sinatra was. Eddie listened to music viscerally without distinguishing words or artists. And there was no sense mentioning the most recent revelations in the Bill Clinton–Monica Lewinsky affair since Eddie didn't even know that Bill Clinton was President of the United States.

"An old man's going up into space," Guy Thompson finally said, stroking his chin like he was stroking a beard, the symbol for "old" in American Sign Language.

Both men had learned some of the more common signs during the many years in which they had been around people with disabilities.

"You ever heard of Senator John Glenn?" Guy Thompson asked. "He was the first man to go all the way around the earth in a spaceship. Now he's going back."

In Eddie's mind, there was the State of Ohio, comprised in its entirety of the southwestern Ohio towns with which he was familiar. He also knew that people like Loolooloo occasionally left Ohio to go to Florida. Fun things happened in Florida, Eddie knew. So, in Eddie's mind, the State of Florida encircled the State of Ohio. That was the world as he understood it. As for outer space, it remained an abstract concept beyond his grasp.

"When you look straight up in the air, that's space," Guy Thompson explained. "When you see airplanes, that's not space yet. That's still air. You keep going; you get to space."

If Eddie had any interest in learning what space was or why people would want to go there, he would have asked, but he didn't.

So Guy Thompson returned to more familiar terrain. "Guess you won't be able to buy a Dodge Ram truck much longer."

"Oh yeah?"

"No more Chrysler Corporation."

"Oh yeah?"

"They got bought out."

"Oh yeah?"

"Mercedes Benz bought them."

"Hate da Mercedes."

But the diversion was short-lived. When a state highway patrolman drove by, Eddie rolled down his window and gave him the finger.

Guy Thompson looked in his rearview mirror to see if the patrolman turned around. He didn't. "That's it," he said, disgusted. "No driving today."

Eddie did not protest.

CHAPTER FIFTY-ONE

The apartment manager feared and disliked Eddie from the moment she first encountered him. He was different, for one thing. And she considered him a troublemaker. Her feelings toward Eddie were quickly absorbed by her daughter and her daughter's friends. As a result, the group of young girls taunted Eddie at every opportunity. They charged at him with their arms waving and their voices raised in a collective screech. Only when he bent over at the waist and covered his ears did they retreat.

To retaliate, Eddie carried buckets of water to the playground and filled the holes worn in the ground beneath the swings. But when the girls discovered that the swings were unusable, they gave no thought as to why, so Eddie told them what he had done. The daughter of the apartment manager complained to her mother, and the manager called Susan.

Soon after that, Melissa called Susan with more bad news. "You need to find a new driver," she said.

Melissa had been taking Eddie to see his tutor in return for a small fee. As far as Melissa could tell, Eddie wasn't making any progress, but that wasn't why she quit.

"I can't deal with the pop cans going out the window," she told Susan.

"You mean he got in the car with more than one?" Susan knew that Eddie threw an occasional can out the window, mostly so that he could watch the driver's reaction.

"He had a whole bag full."

"I'll take him today," Susan said. "It will give me a chance to talk to him."

In addition to the pop cans and the mud puddles under the swings, Susan also wanted to talk to Eddie about reports she had received from more than one of Eddie's employers. Some days he didn't come to work. When he did, he left early.

But as Susan drove to London to pick him up, what was most on her mind was a remark by Loolooloo. "This driving thing is making him too hyper," she had said. Susan agreed. She didn't believe that Eddie had the ability to drive, and she pledged not to help him learn how. At the same time, she recognized that he had a right to pursue a longstanding dream. So while she refused to help him, she also didn't try to stop him or persuade others not to help him. Now she wondered if her decision to remain on the sidelines was the right one.

When Eddie came out of his apartment, she was pleased to see that at least he wasn't carrying pop cans.

As for the subject of the little girls and the playground swings, Eddie got his side of the story on the record before Susan asked about it.

"Rain," he said.

"Rain?"

"Rain on swings."

"You mean it rained on the swings and nowhere else?"

Eddie shrugged his shoulders. Who was he to explain the vagaries of Mother Nature?

"Are the girls teasing you?" Susan asked.

"Yeah."

"What are they doing?"

"Talk loud."

"Sometimes, little kids do that stuff. You're a man, not a child. Just ignore them."

"No."

Susan changed the subject. "Did you go to work today?"

"Two hours."

"You were supposed to work four hours."

"No work," Eddie said, meaning that there was nothing for him to do.

"That's not the way I understand it."

"Reading."

"So you worked two hours and left at ten o'clock because you had reading?"

Eddie said nothing.

"But reading doesn't start until three."

He shrugged his shoulders.

As they approached the Wittenberg campus, Susan inquired as to where he should be dropped off.

"Man," Eddie said.

The "man" was the bronze statue that the students had named "Wally" because it sat atop a reinforcing wall outside the student union.

A few minutes later, Eddie and his tutor entered the small room in the Wittenberg Library, where they usually worked. But when they found that the room was in use by a group of coeds, Eddie burst in.

"My room! Go now," he shouted, waving his arms.

Startled, the girls got up and scurried out.

When Susan later returned to pick up Eddie, his new tutor came right to the point. "I quit," she said.

"Join the crowd," Susan said, disgusted.

CHAPTER FIFTY-TWO

Eddie was in a foul mood, so Guy Thompson emphasized the positive. "For a while there, you were going 45 miles an hour, Eddie. If you could do all your driving on a four-lane highway, I'd think you be fine. And the other day, when you wouldn't drive in the rain, you really impressed me. That was good decision-making." But even though he didn't say so, Guy Thompson was still concerned that Eddie was unable to make the small adjustments that were needed to keep the car squarely in its lane. And he still stared too long into the rearview mirror.

"Take your next right," Guy instructed.

Eddie turned right. But he didn't slow down, and the tires screeched.

The force of the turn pushed Guy Thompson against the door. "Whoa, buddy! What are you doing?"

Eddie laughed, then stomped on the accelerator.

"Stop right now!"

Eddie slammed on the brakes, and both men lurched forward.

Guy Thompson looked in the mirror to make sure another vehicle wasn't approaching. Then he walked around to the driver's side and opened the door. "If you don't take this seriously, I'm not helping you anymore."

Eddie laughed viciously as he climbed out of the car. He banged his open hand on the hood as he walked around to the passenger's side. After he got in, he slammed the door so hard that the whole car shook.

The two men made the short drive back to his apartment in silence.

The next day, Eddie called Guy Thompson. He spoke very softly. "Drive car today?"

"That depends on whether or not you really want to learn to drive."

"Yeah, do."

Guy Thompson thought Eddie might be crying. "We'll try again next week."

The following morning, Eddie went to visit Loolooloo, flashcards in hand.

"She's on vacation," the assistant said. "In Florida."

Eddie showed her his flash cards.

"I'm too busy now," she said. "Maybe tomorrow."

"Loolooloo bad," Eddie said.

Then he walked slowly home with his head bowed. For as long as he could remember, he wanted to drive. He thought he had a plan to do it, too. But it wasn't working. He went to reading class, but still, he couldn't read. He took the driver's test every Saturday, but he still failed. He saved every dime he earned, but it wasn't enough. His dream was dying. He didn't want it to die, and he fought to keep it alive, but it was dying, nonetheless. Discouraged and depressed, Eddie withdrew into his apartment. He didn't call Susan. He didn't visit his friends. And he quit going to work.

But Guy Thompson was a patient man who was accustomed to measuring progress in small increments. The following week, he pulled up in front of Eddie's apartment as scheduled. When Eddie wasn't waiting by the curb, he honked his horn.

Finally, Eddie came out and climbed into the car without making eye contact.

"So, do you want to do this or not?" Guy Thompson asked.

"Yeah, do," Eddie said sadly.

Moments later, Eddie slid glumly behind the wheel. He pushed the accelerator to the floor, and the wheels spun in the loose gravel. Finally, the tires gained traction, and the car lurched onto the road. But he lost control, careened down a small hill, and crashed through a wooden fence. He slammed on the brakes and skidded to a stop.

Only Guy Thompson's seat belt saved him from being launched through the windshield. As it was, his upper torso was propelled forward, and he hit his head hard on the dashboard. For a moment, he was stunned. He touched his fingers to his forehead to see if he was bleeding. He was, but not profusely. Then he got out and inspected the damage, both to his car and to the fence. He removed pieces of wood from the hood and he pried the bumper away from one of the front tires. The car was still drivable, he thought. When he returned his attention to Eddie, he discovered that he had started to walk home. He didn't call after him. And he didn't slow down to offer him a ride.

The student was now without a teacher, both knew.

Later that evening, Eddie opened his safe and withdrew his savings. Slowly and deliberately, he covered the dining room table with a layer of twenty-dollar bills. When it was fully covered, he moved to the kitchen countertops. Soon the dining room and kitchen were bathed in green. Then he picked up one of the twenty-dollar bills and cut it into long strips. The long strips he cut into small squares. He scraped the pile of confetti into his hand and dropped it into the trash can, watching with total concentration as the confetti floated through the air. For several hours, he repeated this ritual. Until the early hours of the morning, the dream of learning how to drive clung faintly to life. Finally, it expired.

For the rest of the night, Eddie stood outside his front door and shined a powerful flashlight into the windows of his neighbors up and down the driveway. When the apartment manager arrived in the morning, a mob of irate tenants circled her office, all demanding immediate action. The manager obliged. She stalked off toward Eddie's apartment, accompanied by an angry entourage that included her daughter.

"You're through, buster," she shouted at Eddie when he opened the door. "I want you outta here by tonight!"

Eddie said nothing. His attention focused more on the crowd than on the manager.

"Did you hear me? You're evicted."

The manager's little girl thrust her head forward and stuck her tongue out at Eddie. When she did, Eddie slapped her.

The tenants gasped and recoiled as one.

"You bastard!" the apartment manager exclaimed, shocked. She grabbed her daughter by the shoulders and pulled her tight against her. "Now I *am* calling the police."

But after Officer Brad responded and again declined to get involved, the manager called Susan. "I want him out of here by tonight!"

CHAPTER FIFTY-THREE

Tony took off work early, rented a truck, and helped Eddie move his stuff to a self-storage unit on the outskirts of London. When they were done, Tony returned the truck and went back to work. Susan picked up Eddie and drove west on U.S. Route 40 toward Springfield, looking for a motel. Eddie sat glumly in the passenger's seat, adrift, exhausted, and discouraged. He was entirely dependent on Susan.

Susan had identified in her mind the location of the motels between London and South Vienna, but the place where she stopped was a place she had forgotten about, probably because it had declined into such a state of disrepair that those units that were still habitable were rented to tenants who otherwise would be homeless. She rented a room for a week. It was grim and sparsely furnished, but it was affordable on Eddie's income which now consisted of a disability check that was no longer complemented by a paycheck.

Susan stayed with Eddie on the first night. For the first few hours, Eddie rocked and paced about the room, then he collapsed onto the bed, exhausted. He slept soundly for the rest of the night while Susan dozed intermittently.

"It felt like he was in a cage, and I was his keeper," she told Tony when he stopped by the next morning.

"Hate da little room," Eddie said.

After Tony left for work, Susan called her supervisor and took the day off. Then she helped Eddie find a job since the several part-time jobs that he still retained were in London and were no longer accessible.

Luckily, jobs were plentiful. In Columbus, workers were in such demand that the manager of a fast-food restaurant had recently closed the drive-through because he couldn't find anyone to man the window. Even in Springfield, which in the previous decades lost several thousand manufacturing jobs to lower-wage southern states, jobs were abundant. "Help wanted ads" consumed multiple pages in the *Springfield News-Sun,* and "Help Wanted" signs were commonplace in virtually all retail establishments.

But Susan didn't rely on the want ads. She called upon friends and acquaintances in Springfield, just as she had used her connections in London. The branch manager at a local employment agency found Eddie a part-time job at a small manufacturer that supplied parts to the sprawling Navistar truck assembly plant just north of town. And a friend at the mental health center found another part-time job for Eddie at Mow-N-Clean, a landscaping and janitorial company started by the center to provide employment opportunities for people suffering from mental illness. (For most of his life, Eddie had been enmeshed in the system of services for people with disabilities, but he was also eligible for mental health services since, on more than one occasion, he had been "dual diagnosed.")

When Eddie wasn't working, Susan helped him look for a new place to stay.

"No more 'partment," Eddie said.

"You've had some nice apartments, though," Susan said.

"Hate da people."

"You just mean you don't want any neighbors."

"No."

"So you want to rent a house, not an apartment?"

"Yeah, do."

"Actually, that might be a good idea," Susan said, thinking that a house might provide an additional buffer zone between Eddie and his neighbors.

"That one," Eddie said, pointing eagerly to a house with a sign in the front yard.

"It's for sale, not for rent," Susan said.

Eddie didn't understand the difference.

"When you rent, you pay money to someone else who actually owns the house. You don't own it," Susan explained. "But when you buy, you pay money to the bank. Then when you pay enough money–after lots of years–the house belongs to you, and you don't have to pay any more money except for taxes."

Eddie knew about taxes. He eagerly awaited his refund every year. But he didn't know about paying off a mortgage.

"Buy house?"

"You make a payment every month, just like rent. Except that eventually, the house belongs to you. When you rent, you're throwing your money away."

"Buy house now," Eddie said. "No throw mimi away no more."

Just like that, a new dream was born.

CHAPTER FIFTY-FOUR

Susan pulled to a stop in front of Eddie's motel room after a long day of house hunting. "I'll come back in the morning and take you to work," she said.

But Eddie didn't get out of the car. "Hate da little room," he said.

"I don't like it either, but it's just temporary."

"Bad play," Eddie said.

Susan thought she knew at least one reason why Eddie was so glum. "You miss your friends in London, don't you?"

"Yeah, do."

"You miss Loolooloo."

"Yeah."

"And Melissa."

"Yeah."

"And Guy Thompson."

Eddie was silent.

Susan remembered an important fact. "Guy Thompson lives in Springfield."

"Wreck the car," Eddie said. A trace of a smile crossed his face.

"That's not funny."

"Hate da new work."

"You've just had a long day. Aren't you tired?"

"Yeah." He yawned.

"Then go to bed."

Eddie climbed slowly out of the car and closed the door weakly.

Susan looked away, once again resisting the temptation to tell him to get back in the car and come home with her. When she heard Eddie close the door to his room, she sped away without looking back.

She returned the next morning as promised. First, she blew the horn. Then she knocked on his door. When he didn't answer, she pushed the door open and went inside. She found Eddie sitting in front of the bathroom door. He held a mangled fork in his hand, and the door was punctured with dozens of holes.

"Hate da little room," Eddie said, dropping the fork.

"Get your things together," Susan said. "I'll be right back." After she went to the office and settled Eddie's account, she used the payphone to call her supervisor and tell her that she would be taking yet another vacation day.

Eddie Fugate had now reached the lowest point in the arc of his life. Years later, Eddie's friends would remind him of his stay in the seedy motel whenever they sensed that he was on the verge of a bad decision. "Be careful," someone would say. "You don't want to end up back in the little room."

Eddie was packed and waiting by the time Susan returned to the room, and they drove west on U.S. Route 40 toward Springfield.

"I didn't tell the man in the office about the door," Susan

said, more to herself than to Eddie. "Maybe I should have, but it seemed like there were worse problems with that room than a busted door."

Eddie ignored the comment. "Hungry," he said, placing a hand on either side of his tummy.

Susan had an idea. "We'll stop at the Meadows," she exclaimed, thumping the wheel.

Unchanged from its 1950s heyday, the Meadows Motel and Restaurant was a favorite among locals.

"Good food," Eddie exclaimed when he was done eating. He leaned forward without lifting the glass from the table and sucked up through the straw a sip of his second lemon soda.

Equally content, Susan smoked a cigarette and thought about the day that Eddie walked away from school carrying a tumbling mat. She remembered that she had picked him up next door in front of the Melody Drive-In Theater.

Eddie slurped the last swallow from the bottom of his glass, and Susan's attention reverted to the present. She decided that the search for a house to buy should be temporarily abandoned until they found a short-term place for Eddie to rent. She circled several ads in the morning edition of the *Springfield News-Sun*, hoping that one would give Eddie the space he needed to prevent the destruction of another motel room.

The first place they visited was an odd little house in a neighborhood with streets named after states, this one being Texas. But Eddie didn't like the house, mostly because he didn't want to rent.

"No throw mimi away no more," he said after the landlord showed them the place.

"This will just be for a short time," Susan said. "Until we find a house to buy."

"You'll just be renting it month to month," the landlord said helpfully.

"No!"

"If you take this place, you can get your stuff out of storage," Susan said.

"One month only," Eddie said.

"Why is he coming to Springfield?" the landlord asked Susan.

"He has a job in Springfield."

For the rest of the day, it bothered her that she hadn't told the landlord the whole story. That evening, she shared her discomfort with Tony.

"Then why don't you call the landlord back," Tony suggested. "Tell him that Eddie slapped the landlord's daughter and shined a flashlight in the neighbors' windows in the middle of the night. I'm sure he'll understand."

"Okay, so I told you instead," Susan said. "Now I feel better."

With Tony's help, Eddie moved in. His mood improved once he was reunited with his belongings. His mood improved further when he received his first paycheck. He cashed it and bought a bicycle at a garage sale.

As he was putting his bicycle away after its maiden voyage, Guy Thompson stopped by to visit. "I heard you moved to town," he said.

Eddie looked at Guy Thompson sheepishly, examining his facial expressions and body language to determine if Guy Thompson was still mad at him. (Eddie never asked how someone was feeling. He could tell just by looking.) After Eddie concluded that Guy Thompson harbored no grudges, he looked out at his car to see if it had been repaired. It hadn't.

"Lucky for you, it's an old car," Guy Thompson said. "So I'm just driving it that way."

The subject of the wrecked car was now closed as far as Eddie was concerned.

"Buy house," Eddie said. "No throw mimi away no more."

"Are you buying this place?"

"Buy new play."

CHAPTER FIFTY-FIVE

To help with the search for a home, Susan enlisted the services of Martha Hughes, a friend who was also a part-time realtor. From the first moment he met her, Eddie called her "Big Redhead," partly because her name was hard for him to pronounce and partly because she had brilliant auburn hair.

Eddie made sure that Big Redhead understood the urgency of the situation. "I three five," he said, holding up three fingers, then adding two more. "I man. Want house. My house."

"I'll do everything I can to help you," Big Redhead said. "What kind of place are you looking for?"

"One floor, no stairs."

"That's easy."

"No stairs," he said again. "Ball big."

Big Redhead didn't understand.

"He once had hernia surgery," Susan said.

This cryptic explanation was sufficient for Big Redhead to determine that the matter was best left unpursued. "What else do you want?"

"Slab. No basement," Eddie said, waving his hands in front of him like an umpire making the safe sign.

"How many bedrooms?"

"Two," Eddie said. "One sleety. One office," meaning one room to sleep in and one for an office. "One bathroom only."

"That's unusual," Big Redhead said. "Usually, people want more than one."

"No roommate," Eddie said, making the safe sign again.

Susan explained. "Two people can live in a house with two bathrooms. Eddie wants to make sure he always lives alone."

"No neighbors," Eddie said.

"That's going to be harder," Big Redhead said.

Eddie's goal to own his own home quickly became a new obsession. He called Big Redhead several times each day, once at 4:30 a.m. after she encouraged him to "call anytime." He studied the real estate section of the *Springfield News-Sun* and collected real estate flyers and booklets from display racks all over town. Several times a week, he went with Big Redhead to look at houses. Eddie rejected one house because it was next to a veterinary clinic. "Hate da dogs," he said. He ruled out another because it had a large outside antenna erected in the days before cable television. Others he eliminated because they had too many bathrooms, a basement, or the wrong color roof (dark brown roofs only). So the search continued.

CHAPTER FIFTY-SIX

W hen an administrator at the county's Board of
Mental Retardation learned that Eddie was
working two jobs and trying to buy a home, he
became resigned to the fact that Eddie was back in Springfield
to stay. (When he moved from the group home in South Vienna
to his apartment in London, he moved to another county and
thus to a different jurisdiction.) His case was reactivated and
assigned to one of the newer workers.

Bonnie Jenkins was a masculine woman with a high-
pitched voice who favored jeans and a faded sweatshirt. She
eschewed makeup and kept her hair short and clean but
unkempt in the manner of a woman for whom attracting a
mate was not a concern. While Big Redhead was helping Eddie
look for a house, Bonnie helped Eddie look for financing.
Together, they visited several banks. At most banks, they were
discouraged from filling out an application, but at one bank,
they were told that a loan would be considered if a down
payment could be secured.

"Do you know what a down payment is?" Bonnie asked Eddie when they were back in the car.

"No."

"It means you need to supply part of the money before the bank will loan you the rest."

Later that evening, Eddie asked Guy Thompson for his interpretation.

"A down payment means you have to give the bank some money."

"No mimi," Eddie said. "Broke."

"Not too long ago, you had a lotta money. You shouldn't have cut it up."

"Fuck you, Guy Thompson."

Eddie was not a person who second-guessed himself.

"I'm just telling you the truth."

"Hate da Bonnie-Girl."

Eddie often added *girl* to the name of any female friend if nothing more descriptive came to mind.

"Who's Bonnie?"

"New girl."

"Is she the one who told you about the down payment?"

"Yeah."

"You don't like her because she told you something you didn't want to hear."

After several weeks had passed without progress, Susan started to have second thoughts. "My mistake was telling Eddie I'd help him get a house," she told Tony one night.

It wasn't a statement that Tony was supposed to react to, so he didn't.

"I should have said, 'Ed, you could never own a house. You're not like real people. You can't drive a car. You can't hold a job. What makes you think you could ever own a house? You should just get used to living in an apartment and doing nothing for the rest of your life.'"

Tony watched Susan fondly. He knew why she was upset. "If you were a banker, would you loan him the money?"

"Of course, I would."

"So, you yourself regard Eddie Fugate as a good risk."

"Absolutely."

"Because he handles money so well."

"Because he gets a disability check, and he has two jobs."

Tony wanted to avoid an argument, so he changed the subject. "Won't your friend Mary be back soon? Why don't you get her involved?"

Mary Brandstetter was the director of WeMIB. She had been on maternity leave after the birth of her fourth child but would soon return to work.

"Why didn't I think of that?" Susan said. "Finally, the man makes a contribution to the conversation."

But Tony's contribution would not be needed. Eddie would talk to Mary first.

CHAPTER FIFTY-SEVEN

In the pre-dawn darkness, the staff stood in knots in front of the cavernous building that was once part of a regional chain of discount stores but now housed WeMIB. Some talked. Some sipped coffee. Others smoked a last cigarette. All were waiting for the arrival of the half-dozen yellow buses that were traversing the county to collect bleary-eyed consumers.

From the one small window in her office, Mary Brandstetter looked out at the scene that she knew would be unchanged despite a four-month absence. She took another sip of coffee but quickly pushed the cup away. She'd cut back on her caffeine habit during her maternity leave and thought she had the problem licked, but now she knew that she didn't. It was her third cup of coffee since she had arrived to begin the first of four ten-hour days, a schedule that would permit her to spend the fifth day volunteering at her youngest daughter's school.

The only one of five children to attend college, Mary was a graduate of the University of Cincinnati, where she met her husband, a mechanical engineer who worked his way through college like she did. Although she was barely five feet tall, she was a mighty woman. Blessed by experience and common sense, Mary moved quickly to the heart of any issue and just as quickly to resolution.

When at last the buses converged on the workshop, the trip that, for some passengers, began more than two hours earlier was over. Staff met at the front of the bus, those who were ambulatory, and at the rear, those who were in wheelchairs.

The phone rang, and Mary picked it up, speaking in a raspy voice that contained a hint of hesitation. On the other end of the line, there awaited the first in a succession of parents or caregivers who wanted Mary to solve a problem. She listened patiently, jotting notes and asking the few questions necessary to resolve various issues related to the management of the caller's daughter. But when the mother began to repeat herself, Mary gently cut her off. "This is my first day back," she told the woman. "And there's another person waiting to see me."

Then Mary ushered into her office the social worker from the Sharonview Nursing Home in South Vienna.

"I think someone is eating Bert's food," the social worker said.

Bert had resided for many years at the Orient State Institute but now lived at Sharonview. On that day fifteen years before, when Tony stood in front of Shoemaker's Market and watched in awe as the busload of Orient residents was delivered to Sharonview, Bert was among the passengers. Today he was on a bus again, this time delivered to WeMIB.

"Didn't Bert have this problem once before?" Mary asked.

"He did. He trades the lunch that we pack for him for sweet stuff."

"Which isn't good since he's diabetic."

"Exactly."

Mary and the social worker quickly agreed on a plan to address Bert's issue. As Mary accompanied the worker to the front door, she heard a familiar voice calling in the distance.

"Mary Ann! Mary Ann!"

Only Eddie Fugate called her "Mary Ann," although she didn't know why since her middle name wasn't "Ann."

He rushed toward her.

"What are you doing here?" Mary asked, surprised.

Almost a decade earlier, it was Mary who chose Eddie to participate in the process through which he obtained his first apartment and his first community job. But only rarely had Eddie visited WeMIB in the years since, partly because of the acrimony associated with his earlier participation in the program and partly because he didn't like to be around people with disabilities.

"Need mimi now," Eddie said.

"You always need money," Mary said.

"Buy house. Need mimi. Mary Ann help me."

Mary could tell that Eddie was about to cry. "Come in and sit down, Eddie," she said.

As they sat down, Mary heard herself paged to the back of the building, but she ignored it. She listened as Eddie told her about moving to Springfield and looking for a house.

"Big Redhead help me," Eddie said. "New girl help. Mary help too."

"I don't know if I can help," Mary said. "But I'll at least talk to Susan."

"Good, good," Eddie said, pleased.

Mary heard herself paged again, and she started the long trek to the back of the building. For the first time, she felt a twinge of pain in her leg, and she massaged her hip absently as she exchanged greetings with people along the way.

"We're glad to have you back."

"Glad to be back."

"How's the baby?"

"Fine."

At the area known as "water pack," she stopped to watch. Several consumers plunged absorbent Styrofoam blocks into a tank of water, saturating them. Others ran the blocks through a shrink wrap machine, then workers at the end of the line packaged them in small boxes for delivery to a longtime customer in the floral industry.

When she heard approaching in the distance, the sound that reminded her of a vacuum cleaner, Mary looked up to find the middle-aged man from whom the familiar noise emanated. "You've lost some weight, Buddy," Mary said. "You look great."

Buddy was without speech, and his gaze was directed into the distance, but the momentary gleam in his eye registered its intended effect on Mary. She knew he was glad to see her. Then Buddy continued on his way to her office, where he would take a seat at the small conference table next to her desk, part of a longstanding routine that had not varied even during her absence.

Mary again moved toward her destination, and again the twinge in her leg made its presence felt. She was aware that she was now walking with a slight limp.

She stopped briefly at the job site known as "YSI," so named because of the instrument company in nearby Yellow Springs that was another longtime customer. Both the YSI and water pack jobs provided piecework opportunities to lower functioning workers, some of whom would earn a hundred dollars a month while others would earn as little as a nickel or a quarter.

And so the day proceeded. At noontime, she dropped her brown bag lunch on the table and lowered herself gingerly into a chair, sitting down for the first time since she was called away from her desk several hours earlier. Again, she massaged her hip, but when she looked down to examine her leg for signs of bruising, she identified the cause of her problem. She was, she noticed for the first time, wearing one high heel and one flat.

CHAPTER FIFTY-EIGHT

"Good news," Bonnie told Eddie. "Home City Savings is willing to consider making you a loan."

The Home City Federal Savings Bank was a small financial institution that followed the quaint practice of managing its own loan portfolio.

"Get mimi now," Eddie said.

"It's not that easy," Bonnie said. "You need to collect some documentation first."

"No more paperwork. Hate da paperwork."

"We don't need to fill out more papers, at least not yet," Bonnie said. "But the bank needs five pay stubs."

"Cut up."

Eddie often destroyed the pay stubs after he cashed his check.

"If you bring them to me, I'll save them for you."

Eddie agreed reluctantly.

Even though the bank was considering Eddie's application, Bonnie was pessimistic that the loan would actually be approved, and Eddie sensed her negativity. If she didn't really believe the "good news," then he didn't either. Further action was needed, he decided.

Eddie had learned from experience that when he proclaimed that an event would occur, then sometimes it actually came to pass. "I eat at Susan's house today," he had told Susan recently. And sure enough, Susan extended an invitation.

This time, he put his declaration in writing. On a large piece of cardboard, he inscribed the simple statement: "I'm moving." At the bottom, he printed the ostensible moving date, then on another piece of cardboard, he drew a large "smiley face." Both signs he nailed to the front of his house.

The reaction was predictable.

"Be patient," Susan said.

"These things take time," Big Redhead said.

"I'm trying to find money for a down payment," Mary said.

Eddie regarded Mary's statement in particular as good news, and he was reassured. But when the date came and went, he crossed it out and inserted a new one. And when that date passed, again he inscribed a new one, but he took down the smiley face. In its place, he posted a vaguely disconcerting message apparently copied from a retirement card, or so Susan speculated when she saw it:

So you're 65
Congratulations.
We're going to miss you.
You're getting the hell out of here.

To demonstrate that he was serious about the new deadline, he packed all of his belongings back into cardboard boxes. Except for the small bench that he slept on, he moved all of his furniture and all the boxes into the foyer of the small house.

But still, there was no progress.

When the next deadline passed, he increased the pressure. He stopped taking showers. His failure to bathe was first noticed by his supervisor at Mow-N-Clean. Although bad hygiene was not uncommon among the employees under her supervision, Eddie's ripened condition still stopped her in her tracks.

"You must have a skunk gland in there somewhere," she said. "Go home and take a shower."

"Can't," Eddie said.

"Why not?"

"No own water."

When Eddie returned to work the next day without having bathed, the supervisor fired him on the spot. But two days later, she realized that Eddie was her best worker, so she rehired him and bought him a Coke to welcome him back. He drank it down and asked for another. But instead of purchasing a second beverage, the supervisor filled the empty can with water and handed it back to him. He poured it out on the floor, and she fired him for good.

That night, after Eddie got home, he removed the light bulbs from the overhead fixtures in each room and threw them into the street. When Bonnie arrived the next day, she noticed the grin on Eddie's face but not the light bulbs in the street. So Eddie took her by the arm and showed her the sheen of glass that by now was enmeshed in the pavement.

"What's that?"

"Light bulbs."

"From your house?"

"Yeah."

"Why'd you do that?"

"No own electric."

When Bonnie stepped inside, she failed to notice that the

floor was wet. Her feet went out from under her, and she landed on her butt.

"Why is the floor all wet?" she asked from her sitting position.

Eddie's eyes went upward, and Bonnie's followed. Droplets of water still clung to the ceiling.

"Bad roof," Eddie said.

Before Bonnie accepted the conclusion toward which she was being led, she looked for evidence to the contrary. On the floor beside her was an empty bucket. She turned it upside down and watched the last few drops of water drain out.

"I think you threw the water up there and dumped the rest on the floor."

Eddie looked down at his feet, attempting unsuccessfully to suppress a smile. "I move now!" he said.

Bonnie righted herself and followed Eddie to the kitchen, where she discovered that Eddie had unplugged the refrigerator and pushed it to the top of the basement stairs. Calmly, she offered the first of two observations. "Your food will spoil."

"Food gone."

Fearful that if she opened the door to see for herself, the refrigerator might tumble down the stairs, she proceeded directly to her second point. "If it falls down the steps, you'll have to pay for it."

"No!"

Bonnie pulled the refrigerator back from the precipice.

"I burn house down!"

Unbeknownst to Eddie, his threat to burn down his house created a sense of urgency that he previously had been unable to impart. Bonnie went back to her office and called Big Redhead. The next day, Big Redhead called Eddie and told him that if he took a bath, she would schedule a formal appointment with him at her office. Eddie took the bait. He arrived freshly scrubbed and wearing his suit. Later that afternoon, Big Redhead found a house that Eddie liked. It had two bedrooms, a garage, and no basement.

Big Redhead submitted an offer, and Eddie assumed the deal was complete.

"No, no," Big Redhead cautioned. "It's just an offer. Now we'll wait to see if the sellers agree to it."

To Eddie's delight, the offer was initially accepted, but shortly thereafter, the deal fell through. When it did, Eddie pushed the refrigerator down the basement stairs.

"You'll have to pay for that," Bonnie told him.

"Bonnie-girl fired," Eddie said.

"You can't fire me," Bonnie said. "You don't sign my paycheck."

"Go now!" Eddie pointed to the door.

After Bonnie left, Eddie called the landlord and told him that he needed a new refrigerator.

"The one you have is almost new," the landlord said.

"Broke," Eddie said.

When the landlord came over to see for himself, he was flummoxed by the site of the crumpled appliance lying at the foot of the basement steps. For a moment, he was speechless.

"Need new 'frigerator," Eddie said, helpfully. But then, in recognition of his own culpability, he moderated his demand. "For pop only," he said, in the spirit of meeting the landlord halfway.

"I'll get you a new refrigerator because the house has to have a refrigerator. But I want you out of here by the end of the month."

"Yeah, yeah," Eddie said, like the rabbit that was thrown into the briar patch.

CHAPTER FIFTY-NINE

Maggie Thornberry understood from an early age that she was not blessed with good looks. She assumed that she would never marry, but then she met Walter, a man in the same circumstance. Together they enjoyed a long and loving relationship that produced several children, all now grown. A few years earlier, Walter was diagnosed with cancer. After a battle that the two of them fought together, he died. Now Maggie was in the midst of her own battle with cancer. At one point, she found herself in the intensive care unit in the same bed in which her husband had lain when he passed away. So powerful was the connection to death that she thought she was going to die too, but she was visited in the middle of the night by an angel who told her that there was work for her still to do.

Maggie had worked at WeMIB for more than thirty years and had planned to retire. Instead, she went back to work. Where before, she had too often measured her performance according to the completion of tasks and assignments, now she concerned herself mostly with nurturing relationships. But after a too-short time, the insidious disease reappeared. Someday the disease would take her too. But not yet.

———

MAGGIE SAT in her paper-strewn office, an office so small that another person could be accommodated only if the door was left open. Exhausted, she sat with her head in her hands. She rested, and she prayed.

Bonnie knocked gently on the doorframe. "Are you okay?"

"I'm fine," Maggie said, rousing herself.

"Eddie fired me," Bonnie said with an awkward chuckle.

The mention of Eddie Fugate infused Maggie with a modicum of energy. "Is that what he told you? That you're fired?"

"That's what he said."

"Has he fired you before?"

"Yeah, but by the next day, he's always been fine. Until today. Today I was still fired."

"I'll talk to him. If he tells me you're fired, then you're fired."

"Isn't that letting the inmates run the asylum?"

"Maybe," Maggie said, ignoring the indelicate analogy.

That night and once a week thereafter, Maggie and Eddie ate pasta at Fazoli's Restaurant. Maggie liked the food, and she knew Eddie would too. But she also liked the place because the manager had hired several WeMIB consumers to circulate among the patrons and hand out free breadsticks.

The free breadsticks, Eddie accepted. The consumers, he ignored.

CHAPTER SIXTY

Shortly after Eddie lost his job at Mow-N-Clean, he also lost his manufacturing job when he barred coworkers from using the break room after he cleaned it.

The next day, he went again to Mary Ann's office.

"Need new work," Eddie said.

"What happened?"

"Fired," Eddie said softly.

"You've been losing an awful lot of jobs, buddy," Mary Ann said calmly.

"Yeah," Eddie said, looking down at the floor.

"If you're not working, you're not gonna buy a house."

"Need *new* work," Eddie said again.

"You could work at the bus garage."

"Hate da workshop."

"It's not the workshop," Mary Ann said, splitting hairs. "It's the building next door to the workshop. You would be a big help to John Reed."

John Reed was the supervisor who ran the place. Eddie liked John, Mary Ann knew.

"He needs a good man to wash buses," Mary Ann said. "Let's go talk to him."

———

JOHN REED HAD WEARY, bloodhound eyes and salt and pepper bangs cut like the Beatles when they first became famous. He was also a man of ever-enlarging girth, which he concealed beneath capacious shirts that he never tucked in. Up before five and into work by six, John Reed shuffled schedules, dispatched buses, and filled in for drivers who didn't show up. Work came naturally to John Reed. So did caring for other people. When his father's health deteriorated, John Reed invited him to move in with him. And when John Reed was asked to provide weekend respite care for children with special needs, he did that too.

"You look like a man who needs a job," John Reed said.

"No more yellow buses," said Eddie.

"You'd be working on the buses, Eddie. Not riding them."

"Workshop check?" Eddie was still suspicious that he would be an employee of the sheltered workshop.

"Yes," John Reed said honestly.

"No work at workshop no more."

"You wouldn't have to do the job forever," John Reed said. "Just until you get something better."

For the first time, it occurred to Mary Ann that Eddie's quest for a home might not have a happy ending. Maybe he wouldn't be able to hold up his end of the bargain.

Eddie saw the look of concern on Mary Ann's face and sensed that she was now questioning the viability of the enterprise. "I do it," he blurted.

And so, three days a week, Eddie cleaned and washed buses. No one worked harder.

Several days later, John Reed learned that Eddie needed a place to stay and suggested to Eddie that he move into a spare bedroom at his house. From the beginning, the two men hit it off. Eddie played Felix to John Reed's Oscar, Eddie being the one who liked everything to be in its place. When John Reed brought groceries in from the car, Eddie put them away. When the trash can was full, Eddie emptied it.

But occasionally, Eddie went too far. When John Reed came home from work, he took off his shoes as soon as he walked in the door. When he did, Eddie picked them up and put them in the closet.

"What did you do with my shoes?" John Reed asked.

"Closet."

"From now on, just leave them alone."

But still, Eddie put the shoes in John Reed's closet.

"Do you want me to start messing with your stuff?" John Reed asked, exasperated.

Finally, Eddie got the message. Except for straightening the laces and tucking them inside, Eddie left John Reed's shoes wherever he decided to take them off.

CHAPTER SIXTY-ONE

The search for a house slowed with the arrival of the Christmas season, but Eddie didn't mind. He loved Christmas. At the group home on the day after Thanksgiving, he always retrieved the large illuminated Santa from the attic and installed it on the front porch, then stowed it back in the attic on Christmas night. He observed the same timetable after he moved to London. While others ate left-over turkey or shopped frantically at Day-After-Thanksgiving sales, Eddie assembled his artificial tree, then hung ornaments and tinsel until it groaned under the weight.

But this year, Eddie's Christmas decorations were in storage.

"Go get Ho Ho," Eddie said to John Reed.

Eddie referred to all Christmas decorations and Christmas presents as "Ho Ho."

"Your stuff is in storage," John Reed said. "But you can use mine."

Together, they hauled several boxes down from the attic.

Then John Reed showed Eddie where to put the tree, and Eddie took over.

Later, Mary Ann invited Eddie and John Reed to her family's annual Christmas open house, extending to Eddie the additional invitation to spend the night.

Eddie marked the date on John Reed's calendar. "Big lunch Friday," he said excitedly.

Mary Ann's open house was an evening affair, but Eddie called all meals "lunch."

"I was invited too," John Reed said.

"Good."

"Four more days," Eddie said the next day.

"Til what?"

"Big lunch Friday."

The night before the big event, Eddie didn't sleep. When John Reed got up to go to work, Eddie was already dressed.

"No work," Eddie said.

"Why aren't you going to work?"

"Big lunch today."

"It's your decision, but if you don't go to work, your mimi will be down."

After John Reed left, Eddie packed a change of clothes in a grocery sack. (He never used any of the suitcases in his *American Tourister* collection.) Then he paced and rocked until John Reed came home from work. When they arrived at Mary Ann's house, Eddie went immediately to the dining room. For the next ninety minutes, he ate slowly but continually.

"Good time," Eddie said to Mary Ann when she came in to inspect the food supply.

"Haven't you had enough to eat?"

"My baby," Eddie said, pointing to his distended stomach.

"You *have* had enough to eat."

"Eat cake?" Eddie asked, pointing hopefully to the gingerbread house created as the centerpiece by Mary Ann and her daughters.

"Not tonight. You can have it tomorrow."

So Eddie went into the living room, lay down on the couch, and went to sleep. He slept so soundly that one guest sought out Mary Ann. "I think maybe he had a seizure," she said.

Mary Ann roused him with some difficulty, then encouraged him to go upstairs to bed.

"Good time," Eddie told Mary Ann the next morning. "Go home now."

"Do you want to take the gingerbread house with you?"

"All gone," Eddie said, looking down at his stomach.

———

AFTER JOHN REED picked up Eddie, he suggested that on the way home, they should stop and do some Christmas shopping. "Why don't you buy presents for Susan and Mary Ann, and Maggie?"

To John's mild surprise, Eddie agreed. He purchased a box of lights for Mary Ann. And he bought straw angels for Maggie and Susan. He delivered Maggie's gift to her as soon as he got home.

"You can do me a favor and put that angel on the top of my tree," Maggie said, obviously pleased.

Eddie gave Susan her angel on Christmas Eve. Many years before, on Eddie's first Christmas in the group home, he made a small angel out of construction paper and yarn. The old angel, now faded and torn, still adorned the top of Susan's Christmas tree.

"Now your old angel has a new friend," Susan said.

Then Eddie opened his presents. New underwear, socks, and shoes he received every year. But he loved the clip-on tie and new sport coat, even though the 44 Short was still too long.

"After we get that shortened, you can wear it to the closing," Susan said.

"Yeah, yeah."

On Christmas Day, Eddie went along on a trip to visit Susan's parents. When they returned in the evening, Eddie insisted that Christmas was "over, done." This time, Susan agreed. "We took the tree down and threw it out the door," Susan told John Reed the next day when she dropped Eddie off at his house.

CHAPTER SIXTY-TWO

When a "For Sale" sign went up in front of a house just a block away from John Reed and two blocks away from Maggie, Eddie called Big Redhead. She didn't answer, so he called her back every five minutes until she did. A walk-through was arranged for later that day.

The asking price was only forty-eight thousand dollars, so it was affordable. And the house met most of Eddie's requirements: three bedrooms, an attached garage, and no basement. But Eddie didn't like the color of the roof (gray, not dark brown), and he objected to the extra half-bath that the owner had created from a closet in the master bedroom.

"One bath only," Eddie said as soon as he saw it.

"So, are you telling me you want to keep looking?" Big Redhead could tell that Eddie was conflicted. "Just because you have an extra half bath doesn't mean you have to use it," she said.

Eddie walked over to the bathroom and shut the door. The search to find a house was over.

The next day, Mary Ann sat down with Eddie, and

together, they made a list of everything he would need in his new house. Including an amount for the down payment, moving expenses, furnishings, and major appliances, the total was seven thousand dollars. "I'm going to ask the Housing Connection for the money," Mary Ann said, referring to a local non-profit organization that provided assistance to people with disabilities.

"Good, good," Eddie said. But he didn't wait for the Housing Connection to act. Instead, he implemented a concurrent plan to raise the money himself. He put his bike he put up for sale for ten thousand dollars.

"You can take the 'For Sale' sign off your bike," Mary Ann told Eddie the next week. "They gave us the money. All we need now is the bank loan."

After Eddie found his house and Mary Ann secured the down payment, the mood of the team was buoyant, but the optimism quickly faded. The bank had still not approved the loan.

"Fuck the bank," Eddie said one evening over supper at Maggie's house.

"We don't talk like that," Maggie said. "Especially at the dinner table."

"No wait no more."

"I don't blame you for being upset, though," Maggie said.

"I burn the house down," Eddie said. "Move back to London."

"No, you won't," Maggie said. "You'd just be hurting yourself."

"Big Redhead is dead," Eddie said, changing the subject.

"She is not dead."

"Oh yeah," Eddie said. "Bad accident."

"She didn't have an accident."

"Oh yeah. Wrecked the car. Went through lillow. In hospital."

"And it's not her fault that you're not in your house yet, if that's why you're mad at her."

"In the hospital," Eddie said. "Leg broke."

"Quit that," Maggie said.

Tempers were short. Nerves were frayed.

Amazingly, it was Eddie who brought the team back into alignment. Perhaps sensing that the tension among the group members was hurting his cause, he smoothed the waters. If before he was short-tempered and demanding, now he was patient and agreeable.

Everyone noticed, but Mary Ann was the first to comment. "Is it just me, or has Eddie turned over a new leaf?"

"I'm seeing tremendous growth," Maggie agreed. "He's much more understanding."

"He's helping more around the house, too," John Reed said. "And he's been shaving every day."

Susan was more skeptical. "He's just kissing ass big time," she said. "He knows what he has to do."

In a last-ditch attempt, Susan organized a meeting at the bank. Maggie and Mary Ann attended too, but Eddie was not invited in case the news was bad. Mary Ann spoke first. As tears welled in her eyes, she briefly reviewed the story of Eddie's life, noting that a child who was institutionalized at age six was now a man on the verge of purchasing his own home. "We owe Eddie this opportunity," she said.

Then it was Susan's turn.

"Every time it's possible to promote a new opportunity for someone with disabilities, we need to seize that opportunity," she said. "We must continue to broaden the network of people who don't hold the old stereotypes and who have a new perception of what's possible."

For his part, the banker was supportive and somewhat bemused. "We'll do it," he said easily, leaving the group with the impression that the decision to loan Eddie the money had already been made.

"When it comes right down to it, people are hungry to help each other," Susan told Tony that night. Then she shared a more intimate thought. "It was so hard after Jack died to let go again, to feel trust," she said. "I couldn't do it for a long time."

CHAPTER SIXTY-THREE

The closing was scheduled for February 25. Eddie marked the date on John Reed's calendar, then recorded the progress by marking an "X" through each passing day. He became more and more agitated as the date approached, rarely sleeping and eating almost nothing. But he remained on his best behavior, fearing that the slightest misdeed would scotch the deal.

By the eve of the closing, Eddie was so wracked with tension that shivers consumed his body. He sat at the dinner table and looked at his empty plate.

"Aren't you going to eat?" John Reed asked.

"No hungry."

"Want me to make you a sandwich?"

Eddie shook his head and looked down at his hands, which were folded in his lap.

After dinner, Eddie went to bed, not because he was tired but because "it probably seemed like the safest thing to do," as Susan later speculated. Except for getting up once to go to the bathroom, he lay on his bed and stared at the ceiling. At 4:00

a.m., he got up and took a shower, shaved, brushed his teeth, and put on his new suit. At 4:30 a.m., he lay back down on his bed.

Five hours later, when Eddie and John Reed arrived for the closing, a large group was already assembled in the conference room of the law offices of William C. Hicks. Mary Ann, Maggie, Susan, and Big Redhead were all present, along with the young couple that were selling the house. (The process had taken so long that they now considered themselves part of the team.) Eddie sat down next to Attorney Hicks.

Bill Hicks was a good-humored and charitable man who, the month before, made his annual appearance as "Symphony Santa" at the annual Christmas concert of the Springfield Symphony Orchestra. Accustomed to working late, his morning arrival was often delayed as he indulged his fondness for reading every comic strip in the *Springfield News-Sun*. When he finished, he chose one of the several ties that were draped around the newel post in the front hall, then tied it when he got in his car.

Attorney Hicks spoke loudly as he addressed the group, partly to project a commanding presence, partly because Eddie was a person with a disability. As he took his seat, he placed a manila file folder on the conference room table. Then he extracted a set of house keys from his pocket and placed them on the table between himself and Eddie.

Eddie focused immediately on the keys. He began to shake, and he wiped tears from his eyes with the butt of each hand. When he could stand it no longer, he reached out to collect the keys.

"Not yet," Attorney Hicks said, covering the keys with his own hand. "The house isn't yours yet."

Eddie's gaze remained fixed on the keys as the attorney continued.

"May I see some identification, please?" Attorney Hicks asked in a formal tone of voice.

Eddie showed him his State of Ohio identification card. Again, he reached for the keys.

"No, no," Attorney Hicks said, "We're just getting started."

Eddie's body shook like a man who was freezing to death. Some in the room thought that he might burst into tears.

When Big Redhead offered him a cinnamon ball to calm him down, Eddie accepted it. Ordinarily, Eddie was not a person who accepted candy (candy was for children, he was a man), but on this occasion, he slid the piece of candy out of its cellophane wrapper and into his mouth. Almost immediately, beads of perspiration appeared across his forehead. Seeking relief, he leaned back in his seat, threw back his head, and breathed through his mouth, the cinnamon ball visible on his tongue.

While Attorney Hicks paused briefly, the women dug frantically in their purses in search of a fresh tissue so that Eddie could spit out his candy. Big Redhead came first to the rescue. She offered Eddie a tissue, and he threw his head forward, propelling the candy directly into it.

With order restored, Attorney Hicks continued. He told Eddie that it was unlawful for the lender to discriminate against him based on his race, color, or national origin. He assured Eddie that "non-public information would not be disclosed by the lender unless authorized by law." And he told Eddie that he had a right to a copy of the appraisal report, "provided that you are willing to pay for it." After each statement, he placed in front of Eddie the appropriate form so that he could acknowledge in writing what he had just heard. Laboriously and slowly, Eddie signed his name to each.

Eddie relaxed as the meeting progressed. He stopped shaking, and a small smile formed on his face. After he signed the last form, he relinquished the pen and rested both hands on top of the table, fingers on both crossed for good luck.

"Do you understand that the amount you owe on the house is forty-three thousand dollars?"

"Yeah, yeah," Eddie said, eyes suddenly big. "Lotta hundred dollars."

"It is a lot of money," Attorney Hicks agreed. "Your payment is due by the fifteenth of each month. If it's late, you will be required to pay a penalty."

"Yeah, yeah."

"And an amount equal to your taxes and insurance has been included in the amount that you will pay."

"Yeah, yeah."

"Your house is not in a flood plain. So that's a good thing."

"Yeah, yeah."

"And there's no penalty if you pay off the loan early."

Except for Eddie, everyone laughed softly.

"Do you have the down payment?"

Eddie extracted the check from his breast pocket and slid it across the table as if it were a fragile object.

Attorney Hicks picked up the keys and handed them to Eddie. "Congratulations!"

Eddie wept openly and brushed the tears off his cheek with the sleeve of his coat. For a long moment, he looked at the keys that he held in his hand. Around him, his friends applauded warmly and wiped away tears of their own.

"Oooooh. Laaa. Deee," Eddie squealed in the high-pitched voice that he used only around people who were his friends.

"You're a homeowner now," someone said.

John Reed presented Eddie with a key chain with Eddie's name engraved on it.

"Oh yeah!"

There was more applause.

"Take six weeks off now," Eddie said. "No work."

"No, no," Susan said. "Maybe you'd take six weeks off if you had a baby, but not if you buy a house."

Eddie laughed, and the crowd dispersed.

On the way out, Susan touched John Reed's arm.

"I just love you, John," Susan said.

"Me too," replied John. Embarrassed, he looked away.

Afterward, Susan, Mary Ann, and Maggie took Eddie to lunch at a restaurant near Mary Ann's office. Eddie ate voraciously, his first decent meal in a week. But then he quickly took leave of the group and went across the street to the workshop, where he showed his keys to everyone in the building.

The next day, Eddie went to the hardware store and had two extra keys made. The first he gave to John Reed, the second to Maggie. Both were pleased that they had earned Eddie's trust, but they were more pleased that Eddie had reached a point where trust was possible.

Later, at Maggie's urging and with her assistance, Eddie sent notes to those who had helped him. A few days later still, John Reed stopped with Eddie at a local florist and suggested that he buy a gift for Big Redhead. While John waited in the car, Eddie delivered several helium-filled balloons to Big Redhead at her office.

"Did she like the balloons?" John Reed asked.

"Hug me," Eddie said.

CHAPTER SIXTY-FOUR

The day after Eddie moved in, he took down all the old curtains and replaced them with blinds. Next, he installed a wireless doorbell, placing the ringer on the wall next to his bed on the theory that the only time he would need a doorbell would be when he was asleep. By his front door, he mounted a red mailbox in the shape of a farmer's barn. Then, in keeping with the tradition established in London, he installed a new front door and a new door into the garage. When he was done, he went to see Mary Ann.

"Mimi gone," he said. "Broke."

"You need to work more hours."

"Yeah, do."

"Maybe you could work more hours at the bus garage."

"No," Eddie said.

"While we look for something more permanent," Mary Ann added.

"Mary Ann, help me find new work?"

"I'll find someone who will," Mary Ann said. "If you'll work more hours at the bus garage. For the next month or so, I know that John Reed could use the extra help."

"Yeah, do," Eddie said.

Eddie spent the extra money as fast as he earned it, buying additional furnishings as well as building materials for home improvement projects. He also expanded his suitcase and vinyl pillow collections.

And he still saw his friends. On Tuesdays, he went to John Reed's house for dinner. On Wednesdays, Eddie and Maggie still ate pasta at Fazoli's. Then on Thursdays, he went over to Maggie's house for dinner. On Sunday mornings, he and Maggie attended the Mennonite Church, and on Sunday afternoons, he walked to John Reed's house to collect the real estate supplement from the Sunday paper. (He still liked to keep abreast of the market.)

Now that Eddie was established in his new routine, Maggie and John Reed organized a housewarming party. At John's urging, Eddie cleaned the house from top to bottom. At Maggie's urging, he purchased a planter at Kroger's, which he displayed on top of the stereo (or, more accurately, the stereo cabinet since the stereo had been removed by a previous owner).

When the time came, Eddie welcomed the guests and eagerly accepted housewarming gifts while Maggie sat nearby and made a list of who brought what so that later she could help Eddie write thank-you notes.

Among the first to arrive was Guy Thompson, who drove up in a new pickup truck.

Eddie met him at the curb.

"Nice flatbed," Eddie said, stroking a fender.

"I thought you'd like it."

"I drive truck!"

"Not this one, you won't."

"Oh, yeah," Eddie said, joking.

"You can't drive the truck, but you can add this to your collection," he said, handing him the now-expired temporary license tag.

"Nice tag!" Eddie said as he passed it along to Maggie.

"Thanks, Guy," Maggie said. "But please don't be upset when you don't get a thank you note."

Sam Goodman brought Eddie some new tools and a leather tool belt like the one he'd worn on the job site. "If your doors start sticking," Sam said, "Don't try to fix it yourself. Call me, and I'll come and help you."

"Yeah, do," Eddie said, appreciating the joke.

Sam took note of Eddie's house for the first time. "Nice house, Eddie!"

"New flatbed, too," Eddie said, pointing to Guy Thompson's new pickup truck.

"Too much! You're doing better than I am," he said before he realized that the truck didn't belong to Eddie.

Loolooloo and Clyde also came over from London. Officer Brad wanted to come, but he had to work.

"Clyde fire me one time," Eddie said, eyes sparkling. A little thing like being fired wasn't something that Eddie took personally.

"You're still my friend, though," Clyde said.

"Yeah," Eddie said, laughing.

"I hear you have a new job," Clyde said.

"Hate da yellow buses," Eddie said.

"It's just temporary until he finds something better," Maggie interjected.

Clyde pulled a ball cap out of a bag and held it so that Eddie could see the logo.

"Dodge Hemi," Eddie said, putting the cap on his head. "Motor big."

Loolooloo was starting to think that the subject of new trucks might rekindle his obsession with driving, so she changed the subject. "Saturday nights just haven't been the same since you moved to Springfield," she said, handing him a gift-wrapped package. "We miss you."

Eddie opened the package quickly, tearing off the paper so that it flew in all directions. "Yeah, yeah! New boom box," he said, holding it up for Maggie to see so that she could add it to the list.

Mayor Henrietta Hochter, Ron Shoemaker, and Fireman Mike all made the trip from South Vienna.

"We all brought food," Henrietta said, presenting Eddie with a homemade pie.

Without saying thank you, Eddie took the pie to his bedroom to remove any temptation on the part of guests to consume a piece. When he returned, he accepted with less enthusiasm the gallon of milk that Ron Shoemaker gave him and the bean soup that Fireman Mike presented. "It was left over from the Corn Festival," Mike said.

Ron sensed the disappointment. "I would have brought you some three-color, except it would have melted," he said.

One guest told Eddie that she planned to write an article that would appear on the website of the Ohio Developmental Disabilities Council. "Maybe if people in other counties see this, they'll do stuff like this too," she said.

Eddie was glad to see them all, but mostly his enthusiasm was directed toward the gifts that they brought with them. For Eddie, nurturing a relationship was not something that he thought about. But many of the guests at the housewarming party would remain a presence in Eddie's life, mostly because Susan would make sure that Eddie stayed connected with them.

Mary Ann was among the last to arrive, telling Eddie that

she had not yet purchased a gift. "I still want to buy you something," she said. "What do you need?"

"New dining room table," Eddie said.

"No, no," Mary Ann replied. "I was thinking of something smaller."

"Bank card," Eddie said.

CHAPTER SIXTY-FIVE

Susan knew what had happened, but she also knew that she couldn't do anything about it until after Eddie was settled in his new home. The apron strings had reattached themselves. At first, she decided not to attend the housewarming, but then she decided that she owed it to Eddie to be there, so she went, but she only stayed a few minutes.

After that, she stayed away. *He has other people around him,* she told herself. And it was true. John Reed and Maggie lived in the same neighborhood. Mary Ann's office was within walking distance, and the new worker, Bonnie, was working out well. But staying away took every ounce of Susan's willpower. To help her keep her distance, she played hour after hour of solitaire on her new home computer. When she was tired of solitaire, she surfed the Internet.

"Last night, I read recipes for forty-two different kinds of vegetable soup," she told Tony one morning.

"Wonderful. Is there a chance that one of these days you'll actually make vegetable soup?"

"Not likely."

But she was stung by the criticism, so she abandoned her computer and threw herself into projects around the house. First, she cleaned the place from top to bottom, then she started on a list of minor repairs that somehow never got made, including patching the cracks in the basement walls. She was mixing a batch of cement in her canner when Eddie called.

"Help me," he said.

"What's wrong, honey?"

"Hate da new work," Eddie said. "You talk, my boss."

"I can't," Susan said. "My cement is hardening."

She hung up the phone and returned to her project. Then she cried and smoked cigarettes and played solitaire all night.

The next day, Susan bought a weed eater and started on the vacant lot next to their house. After a day or two, the gasoline engine exhausted itself, so she replaced it with an electric weed eater. When that too conked out, she went back to one with a gasoline engine. Next, she bought a hedge trimmer. After she finished trimming the bushes and hedges that surrounded the house, she bought a bigger trimmer and started on the magnolia tree. That's when Tony put his foot down.

He unplugged the trimmer.

"Enough is enough," he said. "Why don't you plant some stuff instead of just trimming and cutting?"

"I like that sterile look."

Banned from further yard work, Susan turned her attention to the interior of the house. First, she painted the basement. Then she painted the kitchen ceiling and wall-papered the master bedroom. She wanted to redecorate Christopher's bedroom, but he vetoed the project.

"Why don't we build a basketball court?" he suggested instead.

Susan liked the idea. "The whole neighborhood will use it when it's finished!" she said hopefully.

Tony liked the idea, too. And together, the three of them tackled the project.

"I guess we should have done this ten years ago," Susan said to Tony one evening as together they listened from their family room as Christopher launched shot after shot toward the rim.

"There's no better sound," Tony said, "than the sound of a thumping basketball at twilight."

CHAPTER SIXTY-SIX

Feeling suddenly lonely, Maggie called Eddie. "Want to come over for dinner tonight?"

"Yeah, yeah."

"We'll order pizza," she told Eddie when he arrived. "I don't have the energy to cook."

"Sleety?"

"I'm very tired."

"I tired too."

Then she thought of something that brightened her mood. "What are you doing this weekend?"

"Nuttin'," Eddie said sadly, instantly transforming himself into an object of pity in hopes of soliciting an invitation to an outing or another free meal.

"How'd you like to go to Kentucky with me?"

"In Florida?"

"No, no. It's a lot closer than Florida."

"All day ride?"

"Yep. We'll be gone all day,"

"Yeah, yeah."

On Saturday morning, Eddie and Maggie set out for her small hometown in rural Kentucky. As they approached the Ohio River on U.S. Route 23 near Portsmouth, Ohio, Maggie found herself comforted and protected by the familiar rolling hills that defined the beginning of the Appalachian range. Two hours later, she was home. Deep in coal mining country, the town itself was little changed, too small to attract even the low-grade development characterized by fast food shops. Slowly, she drove up and down the streets of her hometown. She discovered that the house she had lived in as a child was gone, only recently torn down, judging from the freshly groomed clay soil that covered the spot where the house once stood.

"It was right there," Maggie said.

"Big trator move the dirt," Eddie said.

Together, Maggie and Eddie visited the spots where Maggie spent her youth. They went to the playground, and Maggie sat on the swing, where she took refuge as a young girl when she needed to be alone. They stood on the bridge above the creek where Maggie and her friends waded and turned over rocks looking for salamanders. They went to the cemetery and stood for a long time by the family plot, taking in the view from all directions. Along the way, she recounted stories to Eddie, who listened intently.

On the way back, they drove mostly in silence, broken occasionally by recollections that became less frequent as the miles increased.

"I want you to listen to me for a minute," Maggie said as they neared Springfield.

Eddie was listening. She could tell.

"Do you know that I'm very sick?"

"No." Then Eddie corrected himself. "Yeah," he said.

"I'm not going to get better."

"In the dirt?"

"Before too long."

"No!"

"At least my body will be in the dirt. My time is coming."

"Go in the dirt like Jack?"

"Just like Jack." Maggie smiled. In the end, she would be just like Jack.

The next morning, Maggie waited for her daughter Betsy to take her to work. Betsy worked the night shift at a local nursing home. Her shift ended at about the same time that Maggie's started, so she swung by her mother's house and picked her up. Maggie appreciated the ride, treasuring the extra few minutes with her daughter. Plus, she was spared the trek across the parking lot.

"By the way, do you have any money?" Maggie asked her daughter after she opened the door to get out of the car. "I forgot my lunch money."

Betsy laughed softly as she dug around in her purse. When she heard her mother laugh too, she knew that they were both thinking the same thing. "The roles have really changed, haven't they?"

"Do you feel like you're dropping me off at school?"

"Something like that."

"Well, if I'm a bad girl, I'm sure they'll call you," Maggie said, closing the car door behind her.

But it wasn't Betsy who was called. It was the emergency squad.

When Maggie felt ill, she went to the restroom. A coworker found her struggling for breath and called the staff nurse, who administered oxygen while they waited for the emergency squad. As the paramedics wheeled Maggie out of the workshop, her eyes were closed, and her lips moved in prayer. She died on the way to the hospital.

John Reed was one of the first people called. He went immediately to Eddie's house, hoping to catch him before he left to come to work at the bus garage.

"No!" Eddie screamed. Then he saw that John Reed was crying, and he started crying too.

"We should be happy for Maggie," John Reed finally said. "She's up in heaven with her husband."

But Eddie wasn't happy at all. He sobbed and sobbed. John Reed stayed with him for as long as he could, then he told him that the best thing for both of them would be to go to work.

"She'll be proud of you," John Reed said. "You need to be a big man and go to work every day."

So Eddie went to work, but when he continued to cry uncontrollably, John Reed drove him home. Feeling lost, he went over to Maggie's house, where family members welcomed him as one of their own. When they left to make funeral arrangements, they asked Eddie if he wanted to come along, but he went home and called Susan instead.

"My girl died today," Eddie said.

"I'm so sorry," Susan said. "Mary just called and told me."

"No work today."

"Did you tell your boss?"

"Yeah," Eddie said. "No work. One week off."

"A few days, at least, would be good."

"I mad. My girl died. I mad."

"You're sad, is what you are. And that's okay."

Someone once told Susan that anger and sadness were processed in the same part of the brain. She believed that could be true.

Then Eddie changed the subject. "Man come tonight."

Susan was stumped until she remembered that Eddie was getting a new carpet. "Is he coming to take measurements?"

"Yeah," Eddie said. "I mad."

"You're very sad. And so am I."

"No noo-noo tonight," Eddie said, using his word for 'noodles.'

That made Susan cry. Today was Wednesday, pasta night at Fazoli's for Maggie and Eddie.

"Do you want me to take you to eat tonight?"

"No," Eddie said. "Man come." And he hung up.

———

THE FUNERAL SERVICE was held at a local Mennonite church that was pastored by a husband-and-wife team. Mementos were displayed on a table at the front of the sanctuary, including a pocketful of loose change, several favorite cassette tapes, a paperback mystery by Rex Stout, and a bulletin board full of family photos, including her beloved husband, Walter. The sanctuary was full.

After readings of scripture and the singing of several hymns that were unfamiliar to non-members, the female pastor offered her tribute to Maggie, whom it was apparent she had come to know well.

"I know how much you all loved Maggie," the pastor said. "And I know that you are all very sad that you will never see her again."

"Yeah," Eddie said out loud in a voice somewhere between a sob and a moan. He dabbed at his eyes and his nose with the white handkerchief that Susan had slipped into his hand before the service.

Then the pastor wondered what Maggie might be doing in heaven. She had been reunited with her husband, of that she was sure. "She's very happy," she said. "Now she's with Walter. They are together again."

"Yeah, yeah," Eddie said.

"And they're laughing and smiling."

"Yeah, yeah."

"Maggie is so happy that she's probably dancing!"

"No, no, no," Eddie said, shaking his head sadly.

And the congregation laughed a warm and loving laugh. At that moment, they were joined as one. And if tears had not been shed before, now they were.

One by one, worshipers who wanted to speak came to the front of the sanctuary and offered remembrances. Eddie was the last to accept the invitation, but he didn't stand in front of the altar in the manner of the previous speakers. Instead, he stood behind the pastors' lectern. Moaning and sobbing softly, he leafed through the pages of the Bible as though he were looking for a certain passage.

When the pastor sensed that her intervention was needed, she went to his side. As Eddie continued to turn the pages, she put her arm around him and asked the congregation to turn in their pew Bibles to the 23rd Psalm. All joined in reading the passage aloud.

After the service, the mourners adjourned to the basement of the small church, where a home-cooked meal awaited. Eddie sat by himself and ate two helpings of everything, washed down with a large glass of lemonade. Then he went home. For the rest of the day and all night, he measured, cut, and hammered his new carpeting into place.

CHAPTER SIXTY-SEVEN

Although Eddie would not have understood the oft-repeated expression, "A man's home is his castle," the statement expressed one of his core beliefs. As he reshaped the place to fit his idea of what he wanted his home to look like, he sought guidance from no one. During the day, he worked at the bus garage. In the evenings and on weekends, he worked at his house.

First, he decorated the place. Full-color brochures obtained from local automobile dealers he "laminated" with Scotch tape and hung on the walls. In each room, he hung two calendars and at least two clocks. Some he plugged in. Others, he didn't. On each calendar, he marked important dates, including his birthday, dentist appointments, and (curiously) the twice-weekly reading classes at Wittenberg University, which he had abandoned some years before. He also hung pictures of his friends, including Maggie's, which he displayed in a frame alongside her obituary.

In the living room, he constructed a standup desk from pieces of scrap lumber, attaching to the back of the desk a bulletin board on which he taped pieces of paper containing important telephone numbers, many of which he had long ago committed to memory. Next to the front door, he built a plywood shelf where he kept a supply of light bulbs (for reasons that were known) and an electric griddle (for reasons that weren't).

Once he finished decorating, he devoted himself to more substantive improvements. Because he didn't have enough money to buy the materials needed to complete projects after he started them, much of his early work was devoted to tearing things out. First, he removed all the shutters. Next, he removed some of the windows. The ones that he didn't intend to replace, he filled with a piece of plywood cut to size and covered with a black plastic garbage bag.

When he took the shutters down, the neighbors noticed but didn't complain. When windows started to disappear, concern increased. The neighbors talked to John Reed. John Reed talked to Eddie.

"Some of your neighbors are wondering what you are doing."

"My house!"

"Neighbors can help you if you have problems," John Reed said. "But if they get mad at you, they can cause you a lot of problems."

Eddie was unconvinced. John Reed could tell.

"When one of your neighbors waved at you the other day, what did you do?"

"Finger."

"That's what I heard."

Eddie tried hard to keep from smiling.

"Most people don't think that's as funny as you do."

"I laugh," Eddie said. "Ha, ha."

John Reed had several things on his list to talk to Eddie

about, so he moved on. "And here's another thing," he said. "You can't be fooling around in your yard at two o'clock in the morning."

"Oh yeah!"

"When it gets late, why don't you work on projects inside the house?"

Eddie was considering the suggestion. John could tell.

"And you need to quit tearing the windows out."

Eddie looked at John Reed like he had just been told to do the impossible.

John Reed knew that he had pushed Eddie as far as he could. Still, he couldn't resist one last comment. "And for cryin' out loud, put the shutters back up!"

Although Eddie continued to work into the wee hours of the morning, he stayed inside the house when he did. But the advice about re-hanging the shutters sounded too much like a command. Fearful that someone in an official capacity might be dispatched to his house to enforce the dictate, Eddie eliminated the possibility. He cut the shutters into small pieces and threw them out.

Not surprisingly, the condition of the house soon drew the attention of a passing window salesman who found a receptive customer when he knocked on Eddie's door. Eddie invited him in and listened intently to his presentation.

"Five new windows," Eddie said when the man finished.

Eddie selected models from the catalog, showed the salesman where he wanted each to go, and watched with interest as the salesman took measurements. When the salesman provided Eddie with an estimate and described an "easy payment plan," Eddie agreed. When he asked to see Eddie's pay stubs, bank statements, and checkbook, Eddie supplied all of them. But when the salesman examined a blank check, he noticed that two signatures were required.

"Who do I need to talk to about this?" The salesman asked, pointing to the duel-signature lines.

"One name only," Eddie said, pointing to himself.

When the salesman persisted, Eddie referred him to John Reed.

"His only income is disability assistance," John told him inaccurately.

"That's what I was afraid of," the salesman said, dejected.

Other salesmen also identified Eddie as a likely target. When he was solicited over the phone for a contribution to the police benevolent fund, he was happy to oblige since making a pledge implied no further action as far as he was concerned. In response to another solicitation, Eddie subscribed to the New York Times. But when John Reed noticed that copies of the newspaper were piling up in front of Eddie's house, he canceled the subscription. Next, a man from a lawn care company told Eddie that he should have his lawn fertilized on a regular basis. Eddie agreed. When later John Reed noticed a sign in the yard informing passers-by that chemicals had been applied, he talked to Eddie.

"That costs money," he said. "Are you going to pay for it?"

"No."

John Reed canceled the service.

Soon thereafter, a neighbor with a landscaping business volunteered to cut Eddie's grass. Again, Eddie agreed. This time, when John Reed discussed the matter with Eddie, Eddie agreed to pay. John supported the decision, partly because he knew that Eddie hated to cut the grass and partly because he believed the neighbor's involvement might enhance neighborhood harmony.

———

WHEN THE LOWE'S Corporation built a new store in Springfield, Eddie fell in love with it. When Home Depot later opened a store nearby, Eddie split his business between the two establishments. 'Lowes,' he referred to by name. 'Home Depot,' he called the "new play." The stores were five miles away from his home, but he often walked to both.

His first large purchase was a picture window. He picked it out of a catalog and paid for it, then called the store at least once a day until the window arrived. When it did, he walked to the store, put the window on a dolly, walked back home, and installed it. Oddly, the first window that he purchased wasn't a replacement window but a window for a place that previously had no window. Eddie installed the picture window in the garage.

"Why did you put a picture window in the garage?" John Reed asked, dumbfounded.

Eddie laughed. "My house!"

From that point on, Eddie proceeded more conventionally, ordering a large bay window for the living room and four windows for the bedrooms. In less than two months, he saved the money to pay for all of them. When the windows were delivered, Eddie worked non-stop until the job was completed. After he was done, he called Susan. "Windows done now!" he said. Then he called John Reed and Mary Ann and shared the news with them, too.

CHAPTER SIXTY-EIGHT

Because Eddie needed money to pay for his many home improvements, he badgered John Reed to increase his hours. Soon he was working full-time, washing buses and cleaning the facility. But the excellent performance that had characterized his early weeks and months gradually declined. Tasks that he at first conscientiously performed, he now had to be prompted to complete.

"No good day today," he said one day at the conclusion of his shift.

"I noticed," John Reed replied. "You forgot to clean the bathroom."

"Hate da room."

"I know you do, but it's part of your job."

"Need new work."

"You mean you want to work someplace else?"

"Yep."

"You hurt my feelings. I thought you liked working here."

"No more."

Because Eddie had achieved a level of stability in his life

that was a relief to all of his friends, at first, John discounted Eddie's concerns. "You don't need a new job," he said. "You have a good job, and we like having you here."

But when Eddie's agitation increased, and his performance continued to deteriorate, John recognized what would come next. Eddie would intentionally commit an act that he knew would get him fired. He'd already cussed out a bus driver. Damaging one of the buses might be next. He decided to take up the matter with Mary Ann.

"Do you think we could ever find a better job for Eddie, one that he might keep?" John Reed asked Mary Ann one day.

"I think we should try," Mary Ann said.

So Mary Ann called a former WeMIB employee who now worked as a "job developer" for a local social service agency everyone referred to as OIC, short for Opportunities for Individual Change.

"You help Eddie," Mary Ann told Marlo Fox. "And we'll pay for it."

A petite and exotically beautiful young woman with a soft-spoken manner and wisdom beyond her years, Marlo helped Eddie look for a new job while at the same time providing Eddie a "paid work experience" at her agency. She hoped that if Eddie could earn a positive recommendation from his new supervisor, it would help him compete for a job in the community.

From the beginning, Eddie liked Marlo, but he didn't like her car, and he told her so one morning on the way to a job interview.

"Hate da Honda," Eddie said.

"What kind of car do you like?" Marlo asked.

"Dodge Ram Hemi," Eddie said. "Honda bad."

So Marlo was identified in Eddie's mind with her poor

choice of transportation, and he gave her a new last name. Thereafter, he always called her "Marlo Hondacar."

Working together, Eddie and Marlo Hondacar explored many opportunities. Because she knew that Eddie liked to build things, she helped Eddie fill out applications with several home improvement companies, but he was never offered a job.

"How about working at Kroger?" Marlo asked.

"Yeah, yeah."

Marlo helped Eddie fill out an application, and the store manager interviewed him on the spot.

"You'd be bagging groceries," he told him.

"Yeah, yeah."

"And stocking shelves."

"Yeah, yeah."

"And doing some cleaning."

"No mopping," Eddie said.

He didn't get the job.

Then there was the job with a demolition company. Before Marlo asked Eddie if he would be interested in applying, she sought the opinion of John Reed, with whom she had worked at WeMIB.

"Do you think Eddie could do demolition?"

"What kind of demolition?"

"They tear down houses and sell the valuable parts," Marlo said. "It's a family-owned company."

"It sounds almost too good to be true."

"That's what I thought."

In Marlo's presence, Eddie was interviewed first by one family member and then by another.

"They like you," Marlo told Eddie afterward. "When they get the right kind of job, they're going to call you."

"Yeah, yeah."

Later that night, Eddie shared his good news with John Reed. "New work Monday," he said.

"Congratulations."

"Marlo Hondacar do paperwork tomorrow."

"What will you be doing?" John Reed asked, even though he thought he already knew.

"Build new house," Eddie said. "Big house."

"If it's the job Marlo told me about, you won't be building new houses," John Reed said. "You'll be tearing down old houses."

"Tear house down?" Suddenly, Eddie had doubts.

"It's called demolition," John Reed said, pronouncing each syllable distinctly.

"Big trator tear house down?"

"Not a big tractor. At least not in the beginning. You'll go in and tear out the light fixtures, for example. And then they will be sold to people who want to buy them."

"Electric off?"

"The electricity will definitely be off," John Reed assured him. "And the gas and water, too."

"First floor only?"

"I imagine that sometimes you'll have to work on the second floor."

But the owners never called, and Eddie was not disappointed when they didn't.

In the meantime, he worked afternoons at OIC, where he did odd jobs, prepared classrooms and conference rooms for meetings, and cleaned the restrooms, a job he hated. He also made the rounds of all the offices, partly because one of his duties was to empty the wastebaskets but also because he liked to banter with the staff. Exposed to all facets of the operation, he became a conduit of news and gossip. He was among the first to know when someone got pregnant or sick. He looked forward with great anticipation to all birthday celebrations, baby showers, and open houses. And he became the only janitor to ever attend meetings of the board of trustees. So regular was his attendance that the secretary began ordering an extra lunch.

Although it was not immediately apparent, Eddie Fugate had found another home. When the executive director made room in the budget to accommodate Eddie, he became "part of the culture," as the director sometimes described it, working Monday through Friday from one to six. Later, Marlo Hondacar found him another part-time job working two mornings a week at the local senior citizens center. Both were jobs that Eddie would keep.

To demonstrate his fidelity to his new employers, Eddie created and displayed on the inside of his storm door two large signs, both of which were visible from the street. On the first was written in large letters, the name of his employer, OIC, and on the second, in smaller letters, the name of the local senior center. The presence of the signs, combined with the fact that his house was in a continual state of upheaval, led some passers-by to speculate that the two social service agencies had jointly entered the housing rehab business.

CHAPTER SIXTY-NINE

Susan thought later that it was a good thing a chair was nearby when she answered the telephone.

"May I speak to Susan Armstrong?" the caller asked in an eerily familiar voice.

"This is Susan."

"I was told that you might be able to help me," the caller said.

"I'll try."

"Do you know a man named Eddie Fugate?"

"Yes," Susan said, suddenly breathless.

"He's..."

The caller wanted to say, "He's my brother." But she couldn't get it out.

"Yes?" Susan said again. Feeling wobbly, she reached for a chair and collapsed onto it. "To whom am I speaking?"

"I'm Martha Wooten," she said. "But my maiden name was Fugate. Eddie is my...." Again she stumbled. "I'm his sister," she finally said.

For a moment, the two women cried silently.

Then Martha Fugate Wooten filled in a few of the blanks. Recalling the long-ago scene as if it were yesterday, she told Susan about the day when she and her two sisters came home from school and discovered that Eddie was not there to greet them. A woman in a car had picked him up and taken him to the Orient State Institute.

"You mean no one went with him?" Susan asked.

"Nope. And Mama didn't want to talk about it, either. 'It was something that had to be done.' That's all she would say."

Martha explained that, except for Eddie, the rest of the family lived in Richmond, Indiana, only a few hours away. After Eddie was sent to Orient, the family left Cincinnati permanently. "Last year, Mama had a stroke, and we had to put her in a nursing home," Martha said. "And then something changed. In the beginning, we used to talk like Eddie was coming home someday. But he didn't, and we stopped talking about it. After the stroke, it was like we all grew up, somehow. And we started looking for Eddie. My sister found a story on the Internet about Eddie getting a house."

After Susan hung up, she went over to Eddie's house. As his house came into view, she saw him standing on a stepladder by the front door. She pulled up to the curb, and for a moment, she watched as he affixed new house numbers.

She recalled that over the years, Eddie had talked often about his mother. "Momma come today," he would sometimes say, as if wishing it so would make it so. "I don't think she's coming today," Susan always replied, hoping for a visit almost as much as Eddie.

Susan often thought about Eddie's mother. More than once, she had tried to locate her. Amazingly, the search was now over. She wondered what the reunion would be like. Would his mother recognize him? More importantly, she wondered what Eddie's life would be like after the reunion.

Then her thoughts took a negative turn. Why did it take so long for the family to start looking for Eddie? Would they be put off by his disability? Would they stay in his life? Or would the reunion be a one-time event?

"This is ridiculous," she said to herself, slamming the car door as she got out.

Eddie heard the car door close and noticed Susan for the first time. Ordinarily, he would have dropped his tools and walked to meet her halfway. But this time, he didn't. He read something in her body language that froze him where he stood.

"I just had a phone call," Susan said.

But as Susan struggled to get out the words, Eddie saw the deep emotion written across her face. He was the one who spoke the words that Susan struggled to get out.

"Talk my momma?" Eddie asked softly.

Many times during her years with Eddie, Susan had found herself amazed by Eddie's gifts. This was one of those times. "I didn't talk to your momma," Susan said. "But I talked to your sister."

Now it was Eddie who struggled with his emotions. "Talk my sister?"

"Just a few minutes ago."

"Talk momma too?"

"Your momma is sick."

"See doctor?"

"She's seen lots of doctors. Now she lives in a nursing home."

"Oh yeah?"

"All of your sisters want to come and see you."

"Come my house?"

"To your house."

ON THE FOLLOWING SATURDAY MORNING, Eddie got up before dawn, showered, and put on a new shirt and pants that Susan had given him for Christmas. For most of the morning, he stood inside his front door, rocking and watching the street. First, Susan and Tony, then Mary Ann and John Reed arrived to wait with him, all of them pleased that they were invited to be present but apprehensive about the event that would soon occur.

Just before noon, three sisters arrived in a minivan driven by one of the husbands. Eddie threw open his door and rushed to the curb. As one, the three sisters brushed tears from their eyes as they fumbled to get out of the car. One by one, they hugged their brother.

Immediately and completely, Eddie Fugate accepted his sisters back into his life. He motioned for them to follow him inside, and they did. They toured his house, marveling at the work, almost all of which he told them he had done himself.

"I guess you must like the color brown," Martha said.

Susan liked the way that statement came out. It sounded accepting and affirming.

"Dark brown," Eddie corrected.

The sisters asked Eddie lots of questions. And they visited with Susan and Tony and Mary Ann and John Reed. Then everyone went to lunch at Eddie's new favorite restaurant, the Steak and Shake, or as he called it, "Red, White and Black."

As the day progressed, a sense of calm settled over Eddie that surprised his Springfield friends.

"He's so mellow," John Reed said.

"He's almost breathy," Mary Ann said.

"I've never seen him like this," said Susan. "Never."

"I like the family," John Reed whispered to Susan.

"So do I."

———

THE FOLLOWING SATURDAY, Eddie Fugate traveled to Richmond and went to the nursing home with his three sisters. And immediately and completely, he accepted his mother back into his life. The guilt that his sisters felt in varying degrees dissipated, washed away by what they all could tell was the sheer joy that they saw in their brother's eyes.

"Did your mother give you a hug?" Susan asked Eddie when he returned.

"Yeah."

"Did you hug her back?"

"Yeah."

"And did she tell you that she loved you?"

"Yeah."

The rest was left to Susan's imagination.

EPILOGUE

2023

"Take me home," Eddie said to his supervisor at OIC, where he had now worked for twenty years. "Now!"

The supervisor knew that on those occasions when carpenters, plumbers, or electricians were onsite at OIC, Eddie abandoned his assigned duties so that he could watch them work. Today it was a plumbing contractor who had been called, not to OIC but instead to Eddie's house. Knowing that Eddie's demand to go home would be unrelenting, she gave in. "Follow me," she said, motioning Eddie toward the parking lot where her car was parked.

The first thing Eddie saw when they turned onto his block was the several workers who were walking up and down his street with devices that reminded him of metal detectors. But while a closer examination would usually have occurred, what he saw next caused him to give them only a quick glance. That's because a large backhoe was parked in the middle of his front yard. After he got out of the car and approached it, he saw that the backhoe had been used to excavate a hole next to his house, a hole that was deeper than he was tall. He could tell when he looked down into it. "I sorry," he yelled to the man at the bottom of the hole without being heard. The man was feeding a plumber's snake into the sewer line, which he had severed to gain access to it.

Eddie knew that he was the one who caused the clog, and he knew that lots of people were mad at him as a result. But for the moment, he was captivated by the scene. He looked back at the big pile of earth that had been removed to provide access to the sewer. "Big trator move the dirt," he said softly to no one in particular. Then he shifted his gaze to the gray-haired man who was sitting on the edge of the hole with his legs dangling over the side. Joe King was the owner of Joe's Plumbing, he would be told later. "Big trator move the dirt," Eddie said again, this time for Joe's benefit.

"We made quite a hole, didn't we?" Joe said.

Joe wasn't angry; Eddie could tell. This was good. He walked up behind Joe and patted him gently on the top of his head. Then he massaged his shoulders. If Joe thought this was odd, he didn't say so. "I sorry," Eddie said.

"These things happen," Joe said, even though this was the first time in a career that spanned forty years that he had ever been called to someone's house to recover a large amount of currency that the owner had cut up and flushed down his toilet.

"Look in that bucket over there," Joe said, pointing to a bucket that was placed so the man in the hole could get to it. "What do you see?"

"Lotta hundred dollars," Eddie said sheepishly. "Cut," he said, making a scissoring motion with two fingers. Once again, he turned his attention to the man at the bottom of the hole. "I sorry," he yelled again. This time, the man heard him.

"What?" he asked.

"He says he sorry," Joe said.

"Don't worry about it," the man said. "This is our job."

Maybe no one here was mad at him, Eddie thought. Even so, he walked up to every person on the site and apologized sincerely and abjectly to each one.

Now sixty years old, Eddie still lived in the same house that his friends had helped him purchase those many years ago. He still had the same job at OIC, but his janitorial responsibilities had expanded to encompass a campus consisting of four buildings. He still earned the minimum wage for part-time work, with a portion of his paycheck deposited in his savings account to help pay his bills. With the help of his long-time friend who ensured that his bills got paid on time, and with the assistance of support staff assigned by the local board of developmental disabilities to provide transportation to work, take him grocery shopping, and generally look after his well-being, Eddie Fugate continued to live by himself in his own house, just the way he liked it.

Although his failed attempts to learn to drive were now many years in the past, his desire to buy a pickup truck and learn to drive it remained an illusory goal. He still visited automobile dealerships in his spare time. He continued to collect the full-color brochures that the salespeople gave to potential customers (at least until the pandemic, at which time publication ceased). And for reasons known only to him, he constructed several wooden bumpers, at least one of which he apparently planned to affix to the front of his new "flatbed" when finally it magically appeared.

Another long-standing obsession was his continuing affection for vinyl. For many years Eddie spent a portion of his excess cash on vinyl luggage of varying sizes ("baggies," he called them), which he stored like Russian nesting dolls and then arranged in groups, some of which he slept on. But during the pandemic, the years-long practice of directing a portion of his paycheck to his savings account temporarily ceased for reasons that were never explained to Eddie and about which he knew better than to ask lest the error (if that's what it was) be corrected. Suddenly finding himself in possession of a greater amount of cash, the number of baggies that he purchased decreased, and the amount that he saved each month increased. The dream of buying a pickup truck was once again alive.

The week before the debacle with which Eddie was dealing at the moment, he took one of his trusted support staff into the room where he kept his money hidden. She knew that Eddie squirreled away money from every paycheck and that he had done so for many years, but she was shocked to discover that he had saved almost $15,000. Aghast, she reported her discovery to her coworkers, and together, they began suggesting to Eddie ways in which the funds might be spent (depositing the money in the bank was not an option, everyone knew). They told him that if he bought a new flatscreen TV and signed up for internet service, he could watch the do-it-yourself shows that he sometimes watched when he was a guest at someone else's house. Eddie liked the idea, and the staff pursued it. Then they told him he might want to buy a cellphone. He liked this idea, too, even though previous attempts to use cell phones had been unsuccessful. But when it was suggested that he had enough money to pre-pay his burial expenses, Eddie balked. "No, no, no," Eddie said, shaking his head vigorously. "No die," he said. "No die."

Eddie knew about death. People that Eddie loved had died. Jack had been the first and then his friend, Maggie Thornberry. More recently, when Tony Marino died after a long bout with cancer, it was Eddie who lowered his urn into the hole at the

gravesite. Later still, when John Reed died from complications
of weight loss surgery, Eddie attended the funeral, took a
front-row seat next to the family without being invited, and
grieved as deeply and profoundly as they did.

Most recently, Susan had attempted to explain to Eddie
that she had been diagnosed with a treatable form of cancer.
While her prognosis was positive, because her immune system
was compromised, she told Eddie that she was confined to her
house. She couldn't visit Eddie, and Eddie couldn't visit her.
Just as Eddie was unable to bring himself to visit John Reed in
the hospital before he died, so too was he unable to come to
grips with Susan's diagnosis. He assumed her death was immi-
nent, regardless of what she might say.

After Eddie forcefully vetoed the idea of pre-paying his
burial expenses, other equally distasteful suggestions were
made. If he were to die, someone asked, who should inherit his
house?

"You should have a will," someone else observed.

"No, no, no," Eddie said.

These end-of-life discussions were initiated with such
frequency that one of Eddie's lifelong fears was reinforced,
namely that talking about death might actually cause death.
Eddie determined that drastic action was needed if he was to
regain control of his life. He cut up the entirety of his cash and
flushed it down the toilet.

Immediately, he regretted it. This was confirmed when, the
following morning, his support staff discovered what he had
done. They knew because he told them. Then he went to work
and told his coworkers. They knew that Eddie had a penchant
for exaggeration, but because by now he was distraught, they
knew he was telling the truth. The last person that he told was
OIC's executive director, a man who only Eddie called Mikey.

Mikey had already heard about it, so he was ready for

Eddie when he approached. Eddie told Mikey that he was sorry, walked behind him, and gave him the same shoulder massage that he would later bestow on Joe, the plumber. "I sorry, Mikey," he said, choking back tears. (When this episode in the life of Eddie Fugate was later recounted to Mary Brandstetter, now retired, the part about the shoulder massage elicited a chuckle. She herself had been on the receiving end of similar gestures during previous crises.)

Fortunately for Eddie, Mikey had a plan. Having gained considerable experience over the years in the area of home construction and maintenance, Mikey had concluded that the currency probably had not moved too far from the house. With Eddie standing by, Mikey first called the City of Springfield Water and Sewer Department, explained the problem, and called for immediate action. They promised to help. Then Mikey called Joe's Plumbing, a local contractor who had done work for OIC over a period of many years. Joe diverted his people to Eddie's house.

Later, the friend who helped Eddie pay his bills explained to Mikey that on a previous occasion, many years before, when Eddie cut up his money, it was discovered that a process existed to replace damaged currency. Forms had been filled out, the confetti-like pieces were shipped to an office in the U.S. Treasury Department, and many months later, a check was received. It was agreed that the process should be pursued again, although the plan to require Eddie to decontaminate the currency was abandoned when Eddie was unable (or unwilling) to follow the required procedures.

When the bill-paying friend explained to Eddie that instead of cutting up the money, he could have used it to retire his mortgage, Eddie determined that when his money was recovered, he would do exactly that. Mikey would get his money back. The friend would pay off the mortgage. Problem solved.

Closure having been established as far as Eddie was concerned, life returned to something akin to normal. Although his paycheck had been reduced (in a weak moment, he had agreed to resume diverting a portion to his savings account), he still had ample spending money with which to eat out at least once a day. He still frequented local garage sales, looking for baggies to add to his collection. And he looked forward to receiving his annual tax refunds (two checks: one state, one federal) even though the actual receipt was many months away.

As for Joe, the plumber, when Mikey approached him on behalf of Eddie, but without his knowledge to discuss a possible payment plan for a job that Mikey estimated would cost at least $10,000, Joe was unequivocal in his response. "You won't be getting a bill from me," he said. In the weeks that followed, as more and more people learned of Joe's generosity and thanked him for it, he was heard to remark more than once: "I'll be honest. I gotta admire a man who's willing to destroy that much money, just to make a point," he said, even though he was unsure of what exactly that point might be.

ABOUT THE AUTHOR

Geoffrey Steele is a Navy veteran and a retired social worker/administrator. For at least the past ten years, he has served on the Board of Directors of The Abilities Connection (past chair, current vice co-chair), a nonprofit agency that serves people with disabilities by offering safe, inclusive workplaces to thrive. He's a bread baker, birder, and daily dog walker.

ALSO BY GEOFFREY STEELE

The Unstoppable Eddie Fugate

In Search of Ants: and other challenges to domestic equilibrium

Milton Keynes UK
Ingram Content Group UK Ltd.
UKHW041025181024
2218UKWH00002B/137